AAGH! IT'S GOT ME!
GRAB!
LEAP!
D0519348
HAND!
PLINK! A-PLINK! A-PLINK! A-PLONK!
GARPLE! NOW IT'S INSIDE — PLAYIN' THE PIANO!
SCREAM! GOTTA ESCAPE!
AT THE CIRCUS —
UGGLE!
I PUT MY FINGER ON IT, THERE! YOU'VE GOTTA HAND IT TO ME! CHUCKLE!
£2.65

TOPPERTOWN CRICKET CLUB
SCOREBOARD
THIS
BOOK
BELONGS
TO
NAME
ADDRESS
HO
HO

Printed and Published by D. C. THOMSON & CO., LTD., 185 Fleet Street, London EC4A 2HS.

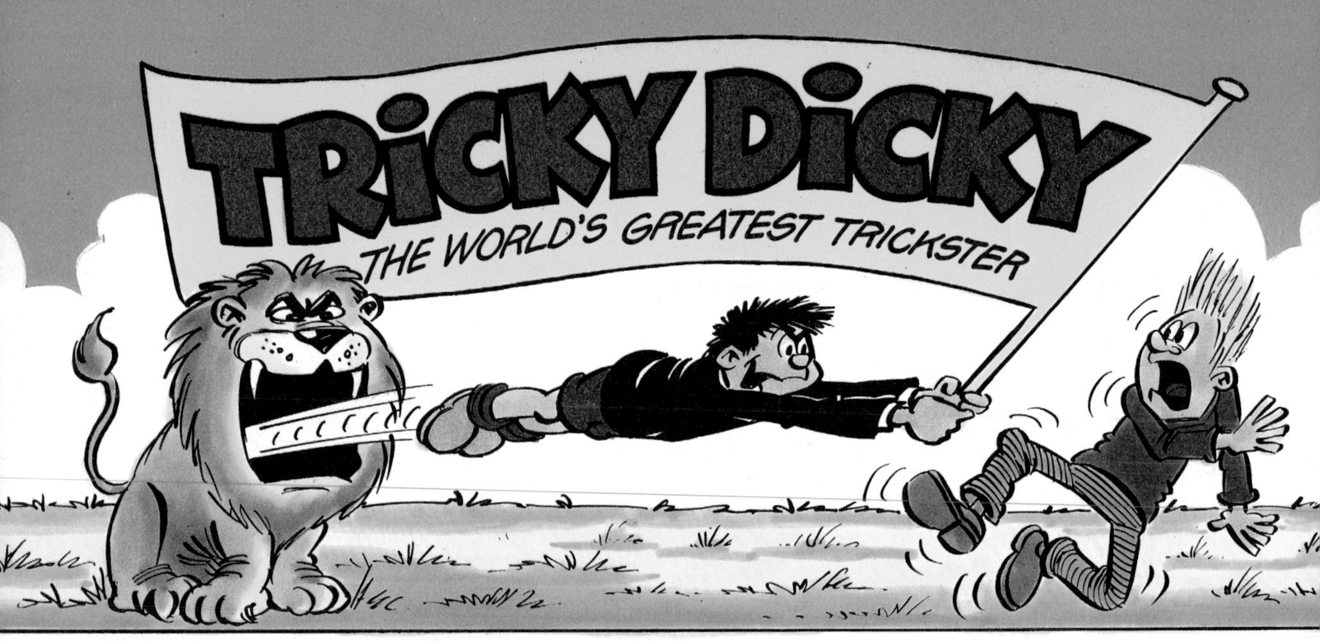
TRiCKY DiCKY
THE WORLD'S GREATEST TRICKSTER

HEH! I'VE GOT LOTS OF FUNNY ANIMAL GAGS TODAY.
DID YOU HEAR THAT CUCKOO, DAD?
WHAT? THAT'S NO CUCKOO!

HEE! HEE! TOLD YOU I HEARD ONE!
CUCKOO!
PROING!
SPROING!
NARFT!

HEH! GAG NUMBER TWO GOING UP!
DOH! OO-ER! WHAT NOW?
CONTROL!
BOING!

IT'S A REAL DIVE-BOMBER! GIGGLE!
WHEE!
BOMB
YEEK!

HAW! HAW! DON'T PANIC, DAD! IT'S JUST A JELLY!
SPLUTCH!
BLOORP!

GRR! GET LOST, DICKY!
HEE! HEE!
CIRCUS

DON'T GO IN THERE, MUM! THERE'S A MOUSE.
DON'T BE SILLY, DICKY.

I'M NOT SCARED OF A SILLY LITTLE . . .

. . . MOUSE! SHREEP! IT'S HUGE!

FLEE!
WAIL! MERCY!
HAW! HAW! ONTO THE NEXT GAG!
SSS!

HEY, DAD, THERE'S A FROG HOPPING ACROSS THE GARDEN.
SO WHAT?

YAAA!
LEAP!
JAB!
CONTROL!
IT'S A BULL-FROG! THAT'S WHAT! HAR! HAR!

DICKY! C'MERE! I WANT A WORD WITH YOU. MUM'S TOLD ME ABOUT THE MOUSE, TOO!
ER — MUST DASH!

LATER . . .
HOLD IT, DAD. THERE'S A SPIDER SPINNING A WEB UP ON THE CEILING.
WELL? THERE'S NOTHING UNUSUAL ABOUT THAT!

FLUMP!
DEPENDS ON THE SIZE OF THE WEB! HAW! HAW!
TUG!
YEEP! TRICKED AGAIN!

HEESH! NOW TO GET THE NEXT GAG OUT.
SCOOT!
ROAR! GET THIS OFF ME!

SOON—
AH-HA! FOUND YOU! NOW, THEN . . .
HANG ON! THERE'S A DOG DIGGING A HOLE IN YOUR GARDEN.

I'M NOT WORRIED ABOUT A DOG DIGGING A A LITTLE HOLE.
WELL, YOU SHOULD BE! LOOK!

AAARGH! MORE TRICKERY! GO AND FETCH MY SLIPPER AT ONCE, BOY!
SCOOP!
HUMPH! WHY DON'T YOU ASK THE DOG?

SUDDENLY—
TRUMPET!
SMASH!
HEH! THAT GOT DAD GOING! THINK I'LL SNEAK OFF — EEK! WHAT?

STOP! COME BACK TO THE CIRCUS, JUMBO!
CRASH!
TOOT!
LEAP!
YEEK! I DON'T BELIEVE THIS!

GNASH! YOU'VE GONE TOO FAR THIS TIME, DICKY!
STOP!
WHEEP!
GRAB!
EH? B-BUT THAT'S NOT ONE OF MY TRICKS, DAD.

NO MORE FIBS! TAKE THAT! AND THAT! AND THAT . . .
OOYAH! HOWL! WHY WON'T YOU BELIEVE ME?

ALI'S BABA
THE BABE WITH THE INVISIBLE BODYGUARD.
BABA DO HOUSEWORK FOR MUM. MAYBE THEN SHE LET BABA WATCH HORRIBLE FILM ON TELLY.
HE MEANS "HORROR FILM".
BABA DUST ALL OVER.
CAREFUL!
BABA USE THIS INSTEAD. MORE FUN . . . MORE NOISY!
WELL, BE CAREFUL . . . GIVE ME A CHANCE TO GET THIS LOT BACK!
AAARGH! WHAT'S UP NOW? ERK! MY CLOUD!
SUCK!
BABA CLEAN AIR.
OOH! IT GONE ALL FOGGY.
BLOW!
CLICK!
I'LL SWITCH FROM SUCK TO BLOW— NOBODY PINCHES MY CLOUD!
BABA! WHAT ARE YOU DOING?
BABA CLEANING FOR YOU, MUM.
WELL, NOW THAT MUM'S HERE, I CAN GET A BIT OF PEACE!
OH, BABA— YOU'VE GOT THIS ON BLOW INSTEAD OF SUCK—THERE!
CLICK!
SUCK!
CAN BABA WATCH HORRIBLE FILM FOR HELPING YOU, MUM?
CERTAINLY NOT! YOU'RE ENOUGH OF A LITTLE HORROR AS IT IS.
AWP! YOU CAN SAY THAT AGAIN.

6 MAGNIFYCENT JOKES
TINY TYPE MAGNIFIED (SAVES ON SPACE!)
THAT'S WHAT COMES OF READING THE PATTERN THROUGH A MAGNIFYING GLASS!
DON'T YOU KNOW IT'S RUDE TO STARE?
AHA! WITH THE HELP OF MY MAGNIFYING GLASS I CAN CLOSE THIS CASE . . .
. . . AND PUT MY SPECTACLES IN MY POCKET! HEE! HEE!
AFTER YOU WITH THE COOKER, JOE!
I'LL BE FINISHED IN ABOUT THREE WEEKS, IF THE WEATHER HOLDS!
YOU CAN HINT AS MUCH AS YOU LIKE, JIMMY — I'M NOT PUTTING ANY MORE FOOD ON YOUR PLATE!
MEANIE!
HOO! HOO! YOUR FACE DOESN'T HALF LOOK FUNNY THROUGH THAT MAGNIFYING GLASS!
BUT THERE'S NO GLASS IN THIS OLD THING!
OOPS!

BOPPO
THE HOPELESS HOOLIGAN
HAW! HAW! A SITTING DUCK! GEROFF THAT WALL.
SHOVE!
WAA!
TOMMY JOE, BOPPO'S ONLY PAL
BAH! I KNEW BOPPO COULDN'T RESIST THAT!
HAWR! TAKE A CLOSE LOOK DOWN THERE!
YOWPS!
BARROOM!
DRAIN REPAIRS
ENJOY YOUR TRIP, WIMP! HEESH!
TSK!
TRIP!
WURF!
SPLATT!
CACKLE! ANOTHER SHRIMPOID TO ANNOY.
WHO? ME?

SOMEFINK FOR ME TER READ? TA!
SNATCH!
OI!
GIMME! UMF! URK!
HEE! HEE!
HIDE!
SHOVE!
DON'T BE ROTTEN, BOPPO.
HAR! FINK I'LL DUMP IT IN THE BIN!
HUMPH!
ON SECOND THOUGHTS, I'LL DUMP HIM IN THE BIN! HAW! HAW!
BOPPO!
STUFF!
BLAGGLE!
GURR! SNORT!
WOT'S IN THIS MAG, ANYWAY? SOPPY STUFF, I'LL BETCHA. HAW!
ULK! J-JUDO! DON'T T-TELL M-ME HE . . .
YUP! I'M A JUDO EXPERT, PAL! BEGONE!
SHREEPS!
FLIP!
WOW!
CLUNG!
HOWL!
BOPPO'S BIN BOPPED AGAIN! GIGGLE!
AAGH! YER CAN'T DO THIS TER THE GREAT BOPPO!
CLANG!
HEH! HEH!
JUDO

SEND FOR
KELLY
AND HIS ASSISTANT
CEDRIC
IN
THE CASE OF THE RUNAWAY ROCKET!

THEY'VE JUST BUILT A TOP -SECRET ROCKET AT THE MINISTRY'S LABORATORY. NIP ALONG, KELLY, OLD BEAN, AND KEEP AN EYE ON IT.
RIGHT AWAY, MINISTER.

SOON, AT THE TOP-SECRET LABORATORY.
THAT'S IT, CEDRIC. WE MUSTN'T LET IT OUT OF OUR SIGHT.

VERY SHORTLY, ON THE HUNT FOR THE ROCKET-SNATCHER . . .
FRESH ICES! HALF-PRICE TO SECRET AGENTS.
ICE CREAM
I SAY, CEDRIC, WE'RE IN LUCK! HALF PRICE ICES, EH?
STRAWBERRY'S MY FAVOURITE.

THERE YOU ARE, GENTS. TWO STRAWBERRY ICES.
THEY SMELL NICE.

WELL, HAVE A PROPER SNIFF! HO! HO!
PLONK!

YUCH! IT'S NOT ICE-CREAM! IT'S STICKY PASTE.
NOW TO SNATCH THE ROCKET.

'BYEE!
STOP, THIEF!
VROOM!
ICE CREAM

THEN—
LOOK! THE ICE-CREAM CART.
YES! AND WHAT SMARTER WAY TO HIDE A ROCKET THAN IN A ROLL OF CARPET.
ICE CREAM

STOP! YOU'RE UNDER ARREST!
WAS THIS THE PATTERN YOU ORDERED, LADY?

GERROFF ME CARPET SAMPLE!
YEEKS!
YUCKS!

BACK AT THE MINISTRY—
NINCOMPOOPS! WE'VE JUST RECEIVED A RANSOM DEMAND. ONE MILLION POUNDS FOR THE ROCKET—OR ELSE!
OR ELSE WHAT?

OR ELSE THE ROCKET WILL BE USED TO BLOW A HOLE IN THE ROYAL MINT!
GOSH! THEN ALL THE MONEY WOULD SPILL OUT.

NOW, GET CRACKING AN' FIND THAT ROCKET BEFORE I RAISE THE ROOF.

NOT FAR AWAY—
NO MISTAKE THIS TIME, MR KELLY! THAT'S THE ROCKET CRAFTILY WRAPPED UP IN BROWN PAPER.
AND THE CRAFTY ROBBER'S DISGUISED HIMSELF!

GOTCHA!
EEK!
ART GALLERY
I'LL HAVE THIS. TA!

LET'S TAKE A PEEK!
OH, NO!

GRAAGH! MY "LAUGHING LADY!"
IT WAS A STATUE. GULP!
CRASH!

VANDALS!
AN HONEST MISTAKE. PLEASE KEEP YOUR HEAD, SIR!
DUCK!

OVER HERE, CEDRIC. THAT POOR CHAP'S GONE TO PIECES.

GULP! THERE'S A LONG DROP THIS SIDE.
AND A SKYLIGHT BELOW.

AND BELOW THAT SKYLIGHT . . .
THERE! I'VE MADE A BOX TO HIDE THE ROCKET IN JUST IN CASE WE'VE GOT TO GO AND BLAST OPEN THE MINT!
SPORTS EQUIPMENT

SUDDENLY—
CRASH!
OOF!
SPORTS EQUIPMENT

WELL, I NEVER! IT'S THE ROCKET-THIEF!
RIGHT! LET'S BOX HIM UP.
SPORTS EQUIPMENT

LET ME OUT!
LATER!
SPORTS EQUIPMENT

LOCK HIM UP, SARGE. WE'LL LOOK AFTER THE ROCKET.
RIGHT, MR KELLY, SIR!
GRR!
SPORTS EQUIPMENT

NOW WE'LL POP ALONG AND SHOW THE MINISTER WE'VE GOT HIS NICE ROCKET BACK.
OH-OH! STEP BACK, MR KELLY—WE DON'T WANT THAT CAR TO HIT THE ROCKET.

EH? OH RIGHT, CEDRIC—BACK!
FIZZ!
HEY! SHOVE OFF! THIS IS MY FIRE!

SUDDENLY, THEY HAVE LIFT-OFF!
YEEPS!
MR KELLY, HOW ON EARTH DID THIS HAPPEN TO US?
A BACK-FIRE, CEDRIC, I THINK!
IGNITION!
BOOM!
I WONDER IF THOSE TWO FOOLS HAVE FOUND THE ROCKET YET?

CRASH!

SUDDENLY, IN THE MINISTER'S OFFICE—
ER—WE JUST DROPPED IN, MINISTER, TO LET YOU SEE WE'VE GOT THE ROCKET BACK.
WE CAME AS QUICKLY AS WE COULD!

Here's someone you may know — who a-perilling will go!
BERYL the PERIL

COME ON, CLOUDS! SNOW! IT IS WINTER, Y'KNOW. YOU'RE SUPPOSED TO SNOW IN WINTER.
FURIOUS HOP!

BUT IN THE MEANTIME —
INDOOR SLEDGING IS BETTER THAN NONE AT ALL. YAHOO!
ZIP!

WHO NEEDS SNOW, ANYHOW?
YELP!
DAD.

QUICK! MOVE, DAD! GIVE ME ROOM TO PASS.
YOOPS!
RACE!

TOO SLOW!
FALL!
BOINK!
FLADOOMP!

DON'T YOU DARE SLEDGE DOWN THE STAIRS AGAIN!
IF YOU INSIST!

TWO TICKS LATER —
YEEKS!
PUSH!
BUMP!
C'N I SLEDGE ROUND THE LIVING-ROOM, THEN?

NO SLEDGING IN THE HOUSE AT ALL!
HEAVE!
BAH! SPOILSPORT!

BUT YOU CAN'T KEEP A PERIL DOWN FOR LONG!
YOIP!
PARK-HOG!
PEST!
YOW!
LEAP!
PUSH!
JUMP!
ROLLER SKATES.
THE PARK'S PERFECT FOR SLEDGIN'!

AND NOT ONLY ON DRY LAND . . !
UNTIE!

VERY SOON —
HOW ABOUT THIS, EH? THE FIRST-EVER WATER-SLEDGE.
COO!
DRIFT!

THEN —
LOST YOUR BALANCE, EH? I THOUGHT THAT MIGHT HAPPEN, GIRLIE.
TIP!
SPLOOSH!
GLOOSH!

OH, WELL, I ALWAYS GET WET SLEDGING, ANYWAY.

ON THE WAY HOME TO DRY OUT —
OHO! A SKI SLOPE? THAT'S FOR ME!
SPROGGIE SPORTS
TRY OUR SKIS BEFORE YOU BUY ON OUR DRI-SKI SLOPE.
ROLL!

AND SO —
YAAAGH!
FLAIL!
ACE!
ZOOM!
HEY!

OUT!
BAH! ROTTERS!
HURL!

HEY! IT'S SNOWING! IT'S REALLY SNOWING!
OH-OH! KEEP AN EYE ON YOUR SLEDGE, BERYL!

COME BACK, SLEDGE — OH, NO!
ERK!
SLIDE!
BRRRRRM!
CRUNCH!

BAH! FIRST, THERE'S A SLEDGE AN' NO SNOW. AND NOW THERE'S SNOW AN' NO SLEDGE!
TRUDGE!

HUNGRY
HORACE

WHY DO YOU WANT YOUR TUMMY MEASURED, HORACE?
'COS I THINK IT'S TOO BIG.

WHAT ON EARTH'S HE UP TO?
ADD . . . DIVIDE . . . TAKE AWAY . . .

YES, I'M TOO FAT. I'M GOING INTO TRAINING.
AMAZING!

NEXT DAY—
HE'S STILL AT IT!
PUFF!
PANT!
WHEW!

HE'S REALLY SERIOUS!
GARSP! GARSP!

SATURDAY . . .
THAT'S FIVE MILES HE'S RUN.
YES, AND NO SIGN OF STOPPING YET.
PUFF! PANT! WHEEZE!

BACK HOME . . .
COO! YOUR TUMMY'S LOST SIX INCHES.
AH! THAT'S BETTER.

NOW I CAN DO IT!

HEH! PA LOCKED THE PANTRY DOOR! THE WINDOW WAS THE ONLY WAY TO GET IN — AN' I DON'T CARE ABOUT GETTIN' OUT! CHOMP! GNASH!

THE TEENY TOPPERS
ERP!
OOPS!
URK!
NEEOWL!
BARK!
SPLOOSH!
...IS THIS SPONGE SOFT ENOUGH? WE WOULDN'T WANT TO SCRATCH YOUR NICE CAR.
BLOF!
SOON—
HOW ABOUT THIS WATER — IT SEEMS TO BE A BIT COO
YANK!
YAAGHLE!
MUST BE THE ICE-CUBES WE PUT IN IT.
NOTHING, EXCEPT VISIT THE SCRAP HEAP FOR THESE OLD PARTS!
OO! CHEEKY PESTS! GET ON WITH THE CAR-WASHIN'!
TEN MINUTES MORE—
WHAT NOW?
WAAH! I CAN'T GRIP WITH THESE SLIPPY SOLES!
SLIP! SLIDE! SLIP! SLIP!
BLOORG!
SLIP! SLIP! SLIP!
SPLUNGE!

I'M TAKING THESE TILL YOU CLEAN THE MESS YOU MADE.
BUT . . .
. . . IT WASN'T . . .
. . . US!
I'LL LOCK THE BIKES IN HERE.
'SCUSE ME, MISTER . . .
LATER, BACK INDOORS . . .
WHOZAT?
KNOCK! KNOCK!
C'N WE WASH THESE BITS IN YOUR BATH?
BLAAGH! MY NEW CAR! WHAT HAVE YOU DONE?
BRRM!
BEEP! BEEP!
ER — WE SEEM TO HAVE WASHED IT A BIT TOO MUCH!
IT'S SHRUNK!
WELL CLEANED.
GLEAM!
ONLY JOKING.
WE'VE FINISHED.
YOUR CAR'S HAD A REALLY GOOD WASH.
I'LL INSPECT IT, THEN.
IN FACT, IT'S SO CLEAN, YOU CAN'T GO IN IT WITH THOSE MUCKY SHOES AND CLOTHES.
HEY!
LIFT!
WE'LL TIDY YOU UP, TOO!
POLISH!
FUME! GNASH! MY CAR!
YOU CERTAINLY CAN'T BLAME US, THIS TIME.
NOPE! NOTHING TO DO WITH US. HEE! HEE!
WONDER WHO PUT THAT MUD THERE?

In 1722, Jacob Roggeveen, a Dutch Admiral exploring in the Pacific Ocean, discovered an unknown island. He named it Easter Island because he sighted it on Easter Day.

EASTER

Mystery Island of the Pacific.

Easter Island lies 2000 miles west of the South American coast, and it is possible that the first natives to settle in the island came by rafts from South America.

No one knows for certain how the natives managed to move the statues over long distances. Some of these statues weighed almost 50 tons, yet they were found 10 miles from the quarry. When a British man-o'-war took one of the statues away in 1868, three hundred Marines were needed to drag it down to the shore.

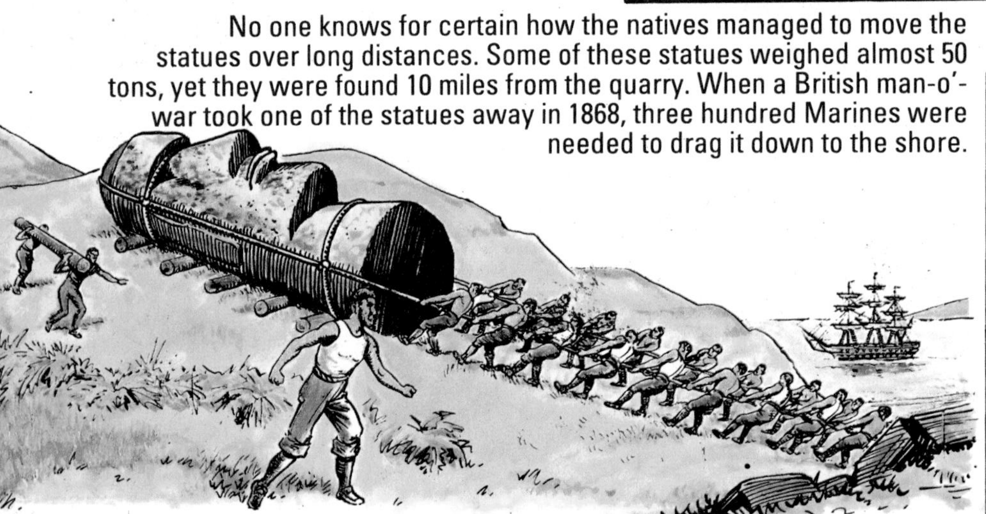

On a certain day at the start of the nesting season, chosen competitors had to swim out to an islet and seach for an egg laid by a particular bird. The first man to bring back an egg to the "Bird Man" was the winner.

When Roggeveen landed on the island, he found two main tribes, the Long Ears, who wore weights in the lobes of their ears, and the Short Ears. Many of the mysterious statues which dotted the island were later thrown down during wars between these two tribes.

Admiral Roggeveen was amazed by the gigantic statues, which stood like huge sentinels on the slopes above the sea. These statues were carved from stone which had been quarried from the crater of an extinct volcano.

At the time when the statues were set up, each one was fitted with a "hat" of red stone. The mysterious people who erected the statues probably got these enormous hats into place by rolling them up slopes of earth piled up to the height of the statues.

In 1862, a slave-ship from Peru carried off the King of the Island and nearly all his subjects to work as slaves on an island near the Peruvian coast. The King and all his wise men died in captivity and the true history of the statues and those who carved them was lost forever.

The few islanders who did remain carried on with their traditional way of life, growing bananas, chilli peppers, and sugar cane, much as they still do today.

AND TALKING ABOUT EASTER...

How would you like to have nothing to eat but Easter eggs? That's just what happened to the crew of a Norwegian ship which was stranded on a barren coast for a fortnight. All they had to eat was their cargo — which happened to be nothing but Easter eggs!

Long ago, many people in England believed that if a house went on fire at Easter, the flames could be put out by throwing eggs on the blaze!

Too many hot-cross buns can make you ill — but in olden days, farmers believed that hot-cross buns cured sick cows!

In olden days, the Kings of England had a busy time on Maundy Thursday, the day before Good Friday, when it was the custom for them to wash the feet of some of their poorest subjects.

At Coleshill, in Warwickshire, it was the custom that any man in the district who caught a hare before ten o'clock on Easter morning was given an unusual reward—a calf's head, one hundred eggs and a sum of money.

On Easter morning, German children have great fun looking for cardboard eggs containing presents left by the "Easter Hare".

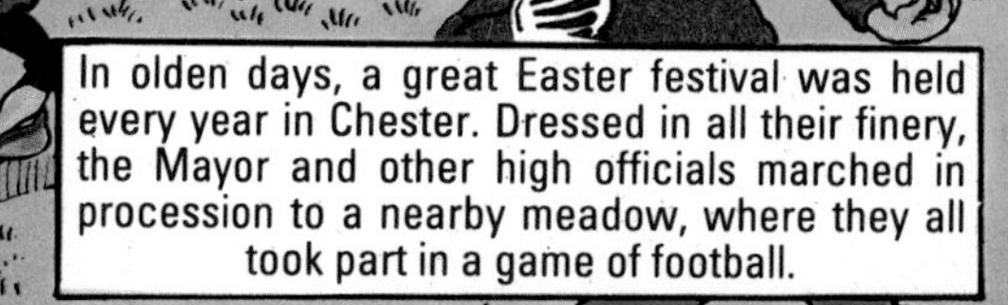

In olden days, a great Easter festival was held every year in Chester. Dressed in all their finery, the Mayor and other high officials marched in procession to a nearby meadow, where they all took part in a game of football.

Desert Island Dick
I'M GLAD THIS GOLFING EQUIPMENT WAS WASHED UP, OLLY. I USED TO BE GOOD AT THE GAME.

PITY THE ISLAND'S SO SMALL. I DON'T WANT TO LOSE THE BALL.

I'LL TIE IT TO THE TREE.

HUH! MISSED!

MISSED AGAIN!
IF HE DOES HIT IT, IT MIGHT HIT HIM BACK!

GRR! I'LL HIT IT THIS TIME!

OH, BOY — WHEN I HIT THEM. I REALLY HIT THEM!
WHACK!
HUH! THERE GOES OUR FOREST!

WHISTLER and his DOG
Whistler's amazing electronic dog, Bonzo, obeys his master's signals, which are tootled out on a specially-tuned whistle.
WHAT? OUR CAR'S BEEN STOLEN?
THIS IS AWFUL. WE WERE TO BE TAKING MUM FOR HER BIRTHDAY TREAT.
IT WAS THERE NOT LONG AGO. BONZO AND I WILL INVESTIGATE.
UP PERISCOPE, BONZO!
TOOT!
VROOOM!
WE'VE CAUGHT UP WITH THE THIEF.
LUMME! I'M BEIN' CHASED! WISH I'D PINCHED A FASTER CAR FOR ME GETAWAY AFTER THE BANK-RAID.
ZOOM!
WHIZZ!
SKIID!
SWERVE!
EEK! I'M OUT OF CONTROL!
CRASH!
GRAB THAT CAR-THIEF!
CAR-THIEF, EH? WOT'S HE GOT IN THAT CASE IN THE BOOT?
GOSH! THE CASE IS FULL OF MONEY!
YUS! LOOKS LIKE LOOT FROM THE BANK-RAID THAT'S JUST BEEN REPORTED. WELL DONE, WHISTLER!

ZZZZZZZT!
NOW I'LL HAVE A PEEP. AH . . . I SEE OUR CAR!
LET'S GO, BONZO!
TOOT! TOOT!
WHOOOSH!
OH, MOTHER! I'M GOING INTO THE CANAL.
SPLASH!
TOOT!
IT'S NOT DIFFICULT FISHING CARS OUT OF CANALS WHEN BONZO'S AROUND!
GLUG!
BLOOP!
BLAST!
NICKED!
DRYING OUT THE CAR
GOSH! A REWARD!
YES! FOR YOU.
BANK MANAGER
THAT EVENING, AT MUM'S BIRTHDAY TREAT—
THIS IS SUPER. WE WERE JUST GOING TO TOM'S TAKEAWAY, BUT HERE WE ARE AT THE RITZY RESTAURANT, THANKS TO WHISTLER.
THANKS TO BONZO, TOO!
SLUURRP!
OIL
MENU

TOM
and
TERRY

SHOULDN'T TAKE US LONG, FRED.
CACKLE! HERE'S WHERE I GIVE TERRY A FRIGHT!

BOO!
SHOVE!
EEK! OW!
TWIST!

TOM! OOH! YOU MADE ME TWIST MY ANKLE! OWW!
GOOD! ER . . . I MEAN, WHAT A PITY — JUST WHEN I WAS GONNA CHALLENGE YOU TO A RACE!
THROB!
HOP!

CHALLENGE ME? SORE ANKLE OR NOT, I NEVER DODGE A CHALLENGE FROM YOU!
JUST AS I HOPED!

RACE YOU TO THE TOP OF PARK HILL! THE LOSER BUYS FISH AND CHIPS. I'LL EVEN GIVE YOU A START.
RIGHT! HUH! EVEN WITH A SORE ANKLE, I'LL LEAVE YOU MILES BEHIND!
HOP!

OFF YOU GO, THEN, TERRY. I'LL GIVE YOU TWENTY YARDS' START. CHORTLE!
HOP! HOP!

OOH, I NEED A REST ALREADY!
FLOP!
HO! HO! GIVING UP, ARE YOU?

NOT AT ALL! ON YOU GO. I'LL STILL BEAT YOU.
HAH!
SCAMPER!

EXCUSE US, GIRLIE, BUT . . .
I KNOW WHY YOU'RE HERE— BUT COULD YOU DO ME A FAVOUR?

FUNNY THING TO ASK, EH, FRED? BUT I SUPPOSE IT'S ALL RIGHT.

PHEW! GASP! PUFF! I'M A LONG WAY AHEAD NOW. TERRY'S GOT NO CHANCE.
STRAIN!

URG!
RUMBLE!
HI, TOM! FINDING IT A BIT OF A CLIMB, ARE YOU?

I WIN! FISH AND CHIPS, WASN'T IT?
PUFF! PHEW! GASP!
ISN'T IT LUCKY I HEARD THE MEN SAYING THEY WERE COMING BACK TO MOVE THE BENCH TO THE TOP OF THE HILL?

WHEN SOPPY SIDNEY BRAITHWAITE TAKES A SWIG OF SOUPER SOUP HE TURNS INTO...
ZAP!
SOUPER BOY
POW!

IT'LL BE YOUR JOB TO TAKE AUNTIE DOT'S DOG FOR A WALK WHILE HE'S STAYING WITH US, SIDNEY.
OK, MUM. C'MON, FROGMOPPIT.
HI!

YEEK! I CAN'T CONTROL THIS POOCH! BUT...
WHEE!
GALLOP!
YAHOO!

...GLOOP! SOUPER BOY CAN!
BEND!
KERPOW!
LET'S GO! LET'S GO!
STRAIN!

YOWP! THIS KID MUSTA BEEN EATING RUNNER-BEANS, OR SOMETHIN'!
HAR! TIME FOR A SOUPER-WALKIE!
DRAG!
SCRAPE!
SOUPER ZIP!

HOW DARE YOU DRAG THAT POOR LITTLE DOGGIE ALONG!
B-BUT... HOWL!
WHAP!
DROP!
PURR!
WOW! A PUSSYCAT!

COME BACK, FROGMOPPIT! YOW!
POOR LITTLE MITE!
BOWF! WOWF!
BASH!
MEEERK!
ZOOM!

HE WON'T GET AWAY FROM SOUPER ME! HEH!
SOUPER BOUND!

BUT—
YERK!
YAARGH!
SMASH!
DOGS' HOME

AARGH! YOU BUFFOON! ALL THE DOGS ARE ESCAPING.
OOPS! I'M IN THE DOG-HOUSE AGAIN!
COO! PLAYMATES!
MOIKLE! I'M OFF!
BOWF!
WOOF! WOOF!

COME BACK! BAH! I'LL HAVE TO BE SUPER-QUICK!
I'VE GOT JUST THE THING FOR HIM WHEN HE BRINGS 'EM BACK.

THAT'S IT! TAKE THEM WALKIES UNTIL ANOTHER LORRY ARRIVES! AN' DON'T LOSE 'EM!
GASP! HELP! AN' I'VE RUN OUT OF SOUPER-SOUP!
ROWF!
PING!
TUG!
STRAIN!
WURF!
PULL!
ROWF!
PANT!

CARROTS THE CONQUERER

JOLLY JOE JAPEMAN runs the brightest, breeziest holiday camp in the whole of Britain. During school holidays, Joe's son, Jimmy — known as Carrots — helps out at the camp.
HOLI
WELCOME TO JOLLY JOE'S. I'M CARROTS JAPEMAN.
HOW DO, SON? HOW DO?
IT WAS SATURDAY, AND A BUS LOAD OF NEW CAMPERS HAD ARRIVED.

EEEK!
CRUNCH
HO! HO! I'M WONDERFUL WILLIE WILLIS. YOU CAN CALL ME WONDER MAN— THAT'S 'COS I'M THE GREATEST! YOU'LL SEE.

WOW! HE'S GOT SOME GRIP! BUT WHAT A BIG-HEADED HORROR HE IS!
BLAH! BOAST! BLAH!
YOU DON'T SAY.

LATER THAT AFTERNOON—
THAT'S FOR ME! I'LL SHOW 'EM. I'M WONDER MAN, YOU KNOW.
JOLLY JOE'S SUPER TALENT COMPETITION!
ARE YOU THE CAMPER WITH THE MOST TALENT? COME ALONG TO THE CAMP THEATRE AND FIND OUT TONIGHT!
I AM THE GREATEST!

THAT NIGHT—
HE'S NOT BAD— BUT WHAT A SHOW-OFF!
SUPER TALENT SHOW! BIG PRIZES!
BRAVO!

SUDDENLY—
THANK YOU FOR HELPING OUT WITH MY ACT, YOUNG MAN.
WHIZZ!
HO! HO!
OUCH!

LADIES AND GENTS — THE WINNER!
OF COURSE!
HUH! I WISH HE'D LOST!

LATER—
THIS WILL BE A WALK-OVER FOR ME. I'LL WIPE THE FLOOR WITH YOU WIMPS.
GRAND SPORTS DAY!
TRACK EVENTS
OBSTACLE RACE
ENTRY FORMS
WE'LL SEE, BIG-HEAD!
HE'S UPSETTING EVERYONE.

THAT NIGHT—
I'M GOING TO MAKE SPORTS DAY A LITTLE BIT MORE EXCITING — FOR WONDER MAN, ANYWAY!

NEXT DAY—
I'M IN FOR THIS, SONNY.
THAT'S YOUR SACK, THEN. GOOD LUCK!
I DON'T NEED LUCK!

SOON—
COME AWAY, NIGEL.
WHAT'S GOING ON?
HOO—HOO! WHAT, INDEED! I COULD TELL HIM — BUT I WON'T!

THEN—
HELP!

HA! HA!
HO! HO!
IT'S ON FIRE!
HOO! HOO! IT'S NOT REALLY ON FIRE. I PUT A TRICK SMOKE-BOMB IN IT!

PITY ABOUT LOSING THE SACK-RACE. WHY DON'T YOU TRY THE HURDLES?
I SHALL! AT LEAST I'LL WIN THAT!

THEY'RE OFF!
ACTUALLY, THIS IS MORE OF AN OBSTACLE RACE THAN A HURDLE RACE. SNIGGER!

IT IS FOR WONDER MAN, ANYWAY!
OOOF!
TUG!
PYOING!

WH—WHAT HAPPENED?
YOU HAD BAD LUCK— YOU HIT THE HURDLE.

SOON, AT THE START OF THE HUNDRED-YARDS SPRINT—
ON YOUR MARKS! GET SET! GO!
THIS'LL BE AN ABSOLUTE PUSH-OVER.

I'M IN THE LEAD ALREADY!

SUDDENLY—
YEEPS!

YOU'RE A REAL SLOW-COACH, MISTER! THE REST OF THE CAMPERS ASKED ME TO GIVE YOU THIS.
GRR!

I'M LEAVING! THEY JUST DON'T SEEM TO REALISE WHAT A WONDERFUL PERSON I AM.
NOW EVERYONE ELSE CAN HAVE A HAPPY HOLIDAY!

SQUARE EYES
THE T.V. FAN
JACK O'NORY.
MERRY CHRISTMAS, ALL YOU VIEWERS!
SAME TO YOU, MISTER. I LOVE THE TELLY.
SUDDENLY—
EH? WHAT'S GONE WRONG?
COME ON, TELLY! WORK! I'M YOUR BEST FRIEND. YOU CAN'T GO BURST ON ME!
DAD EXPLAINS—
THE AERIAL'S FALLEN DOWN — IT'S BEEN READY T'DO THAT FOR AGES.
BAH!
GET OUT ON THAT ROOF AND FIX IT, THEN, DAD!
WITH A FOOT OF SNOW UP THERE? NO CHANCE, JACK — TOO DANGEROUS!
PUSH!
ONE DASH UPSTAIRS AND DOWN AGAIN, LATER—
I'LL HAVE TO USE THE PORTABLE'S INDOOR AERIAL, THEN.

USELESS! IT ISN'T HIGH ENOUGH TO GET A GOOD PICTURE.
CRACKLE
CRACKLE!
HISS!
THAT WAS SORE!

PAH! ROTTEN OBJECT!
HEY! MUM'S HAT WAS BAD ENOUGH WITHOUT THAT!
PLOP!
EELP!

HMM! WE WANT TO WATCH CHRISTMAS TELLY, SAME AS YOU DO, YOU KNOW, JACK.
AND WE NEED A FAIRY ON TOP OF OUR TREE.
EH? I DON'T SEE WHAT THAT HAS TO DO WITH IT!

YOU WILL, LAD. C'MERE!
GRAB!
GRAB!
HEY! NOW, HOLD ON! WAIT!

TWO SECS. LATER—
BAH! MOVE OVER A BIT. I CAN'T SEE THE PICTURE PROPERLY FROM HERE.
HOLD IT JUST THERE, JACK. THE PICTURE'S PERFECT!
T.V. WAND.
TIED

JIMMY JINX AND WHAT HE THINKS

JIMMY! YOU'VE SLEPT IN! YOU'LL BE LATE FOR SCHOOL!
OH, NO!

THIS IS ALWAYS HAPPENING! OH, WHERE ARE MY CLOTHES?

DRESSING TAKES UP TOO MUCH TIME IN THE MORNING.
YOU COULD ALWAYS GO OUT WITHOUT ANY ON!
DON'T BE STUPID!

DRESS ON THE MOVE, JIM! IT'S QUICKER!
MIND THOSE LACES!

NEE-AGH!
TRIP!

OH, WELL, IT'S GOT HIM DOWNSTAIRS FASTER!
SLIDE!
BAH! HE'S SUPPOSED TO WALK DOWN!

STOP UNTIL YOU CAN SEE WHERE YOU'RE GOING, JAMES.
STOP FUSSIN' LIKE AN OLD HEN!
I'M NOT AN OLD HEN!
HUH! AN OLD GRANNY, THEN!
OH, GOLLY! THAT'S OUR FAULT! POOR JAMES!
WE SHOULD'VE BEEN WATCHING.
BASH!

CHEER UP, JIM! I'VE GOT A BRILLIANT IDEA! TOMORROW IT'S ALL GONNA BE DIFFERENT!
OH, YES?
STAGGER!

BED-TIME—
GOIN' TO BED FULLY-DRESSED! THINK OF THE TIME HE'LL SAVE IN THE MORNING!
I DON'T LIKE IT.

NEXT MORNING—
JIMMY! YOU'VE DONE IT AGAIN! GET DRESSED! UP! UP! UP!
YAWN! EH?

JIMMY! STOP!
FOOL!
OH, NO! JIM DID AS DAD SAID! HE FORGOT HE HAD HIS CLOTHES ON, AND GOT DRESSED IN HIS PYJAMAS!

PIRATES!

THE WAYS AND DAYS OF THE 'JOLLY ROGER' BOYS!

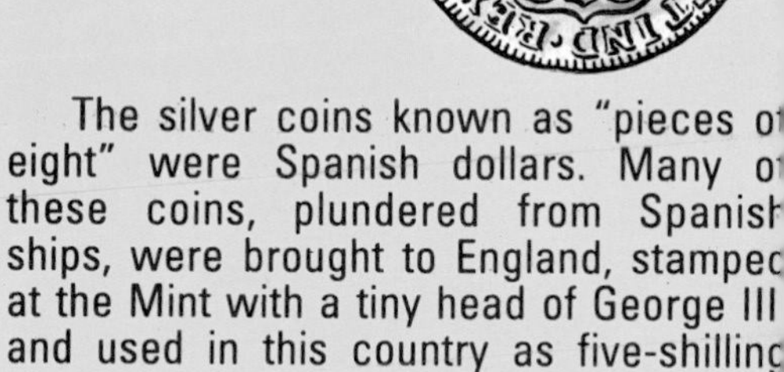

The silver coins known as "pieces of eight" were Spanish dollars. Many of these coins, plundered from Spanish ships, were brought to England, stamped at the Mint with a tiny head of George III and used in this country as five-shilling pieces (25p).

Seamen who were captured by pirates were often given the choice of signing on with the pirate crew — or blowing their own brains out!

Pirates badly hurt in battle received money to make up for their wounds. For instance, about 800 pieces of eight was the usual amount paid for the loss of a leg.

Many pirate crews preferred death to surrender. So, during sea-fights, one man stood by ready to blow up the pirate-ship if it was in danger of capture.

Welshman, Sir Henry Morgan, was born in Monmouthshire in 1635. The greatest triumph of this famous buccaneer was the capture of the Spanish city of Panama. It took 200 mules to carry away the loot from the city.

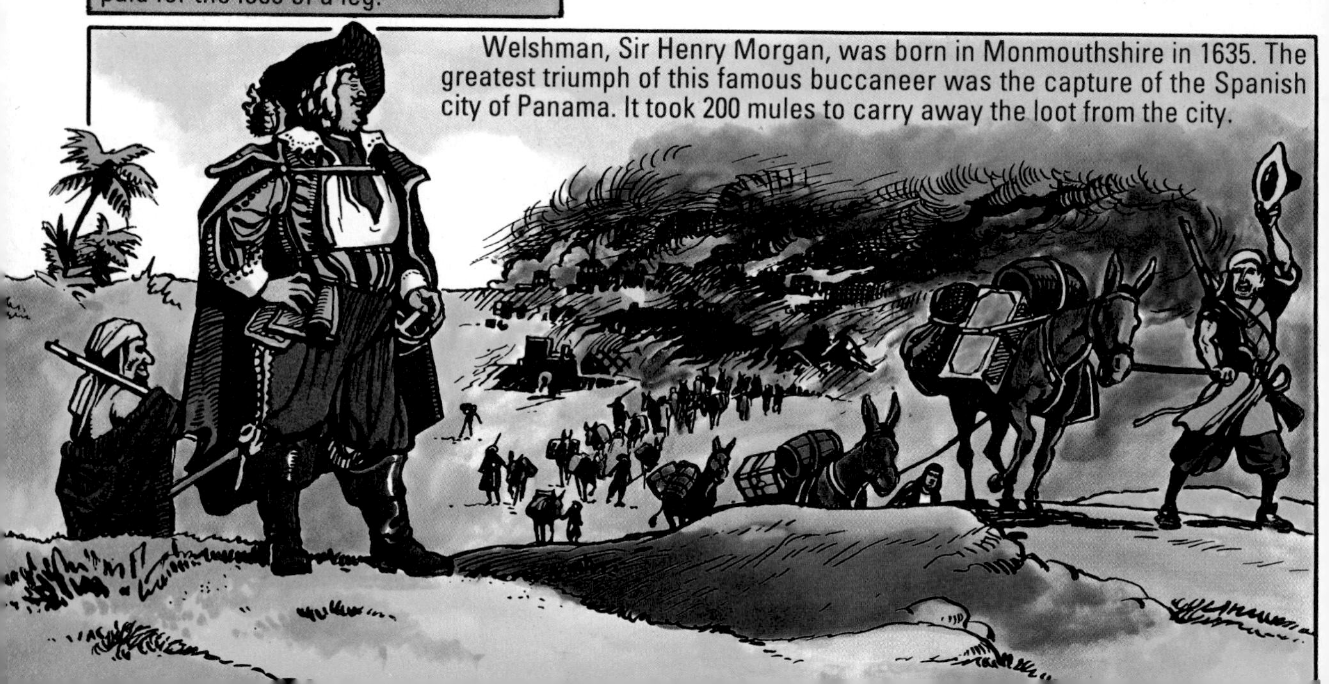

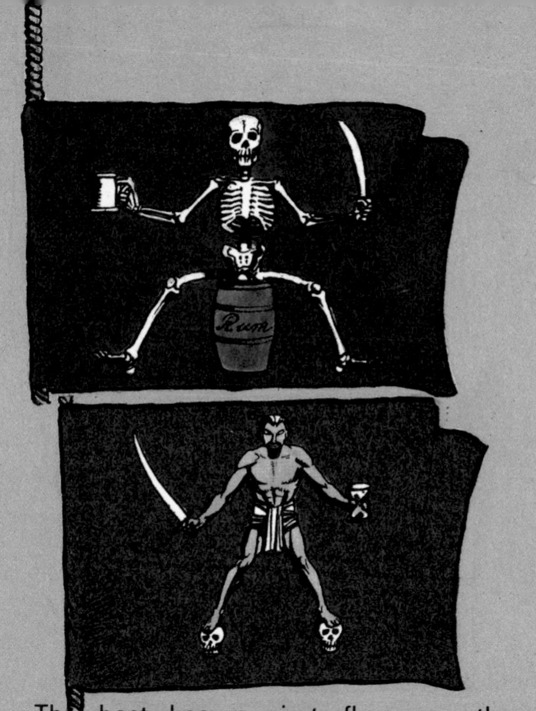

The best known pirate-flag was the skull-and-crossbones or "Jolly Roger." But flags like those shown above were flown by Captain Bartholomew Roberts, who captured more ships than any other pirate.

Captain Teach, known as Blackbeard, came from Bristol. He always went into a fight with lighted matches stuck in the brim of his hat to make himself look more terrifying.

Pierre Le Grand was a daring French pirate who had his headquarters on Tortuga Island, in the West Indies. He became famous when, in a small open boat, he and a few men attacked and captured a huge Spanish treasure ship.

When Blackbeard the Pirate was drinking, his idea of a joke was to fire his pistols under the table where he and his comrades sat. In this way he crippled his shipmate, Israel Hands.

The pirate known as Panther Key John was said to have lived to over a hundred years old. He died in Florida, America, in 1900.

A well-known pirate of the Spanish Main was Captain Greaves, known as "Red Legs". He objected to his captain's cruel treatment of prisoners, overcame him in a knife duel and took command.

Tiny
THE WORLD'S BIGGEST DOG
PHEW! I'M TIRED AFTER THAT WALK, TINY. LET'S CATCH THE BUS HOME.
GASP! GOOD IDEA. I'M TIRED, TOO.
BUS STOP
SO TIRED, I COULD SLEEP. YAWN!

TINY! LOOK OUT! DON'T LEAN ON THE BUS STOP!
OOPS!
BEND!
BUS STOP

AND DON'T LEAN ON ME, EITHER!
LEAN!

AH! HERE'S THE BUS AT LAST!

SORRY, SIR — WE CAN'T HAVE THAT THERE THING INSIDE OUR BUS, WE CAN'T!
EH?

OH, WELL, I KNOW WHAT TO DO!

GREAT!
THAT'S SOLVED IT! ONE AND A DOG, HOME, PLEASE.

IT'LL BE MUCH EASIER TO GET TINY HOME, THIS WAY!

WHEE!

OH, GOSH!

A LOW BRIDGE!

I CAN'T LOOK!
I'LL NOT GET UNDER IT! IT'S GETTING NEARER!
YES, ABSOLUTELY NO TROUBLE NOW!
AAARGH!
WHOOSH!
COO! WHERE'S HE GOING?

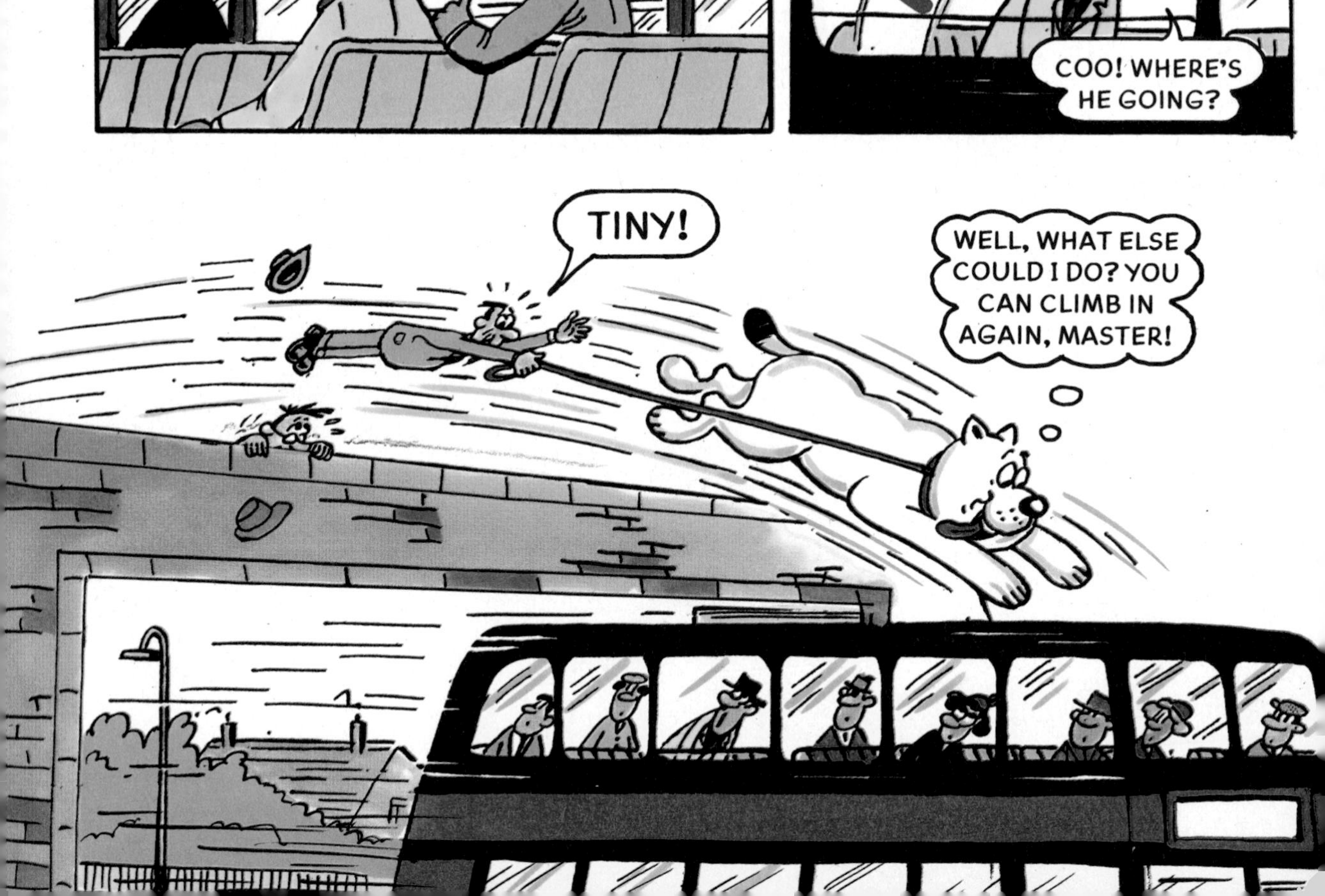
TINY!
WELL, WHAT ELSE COULD I DO? YOU CAN CLIMB IN AGAIN, MASTER!

MICKEY THE MONKEY

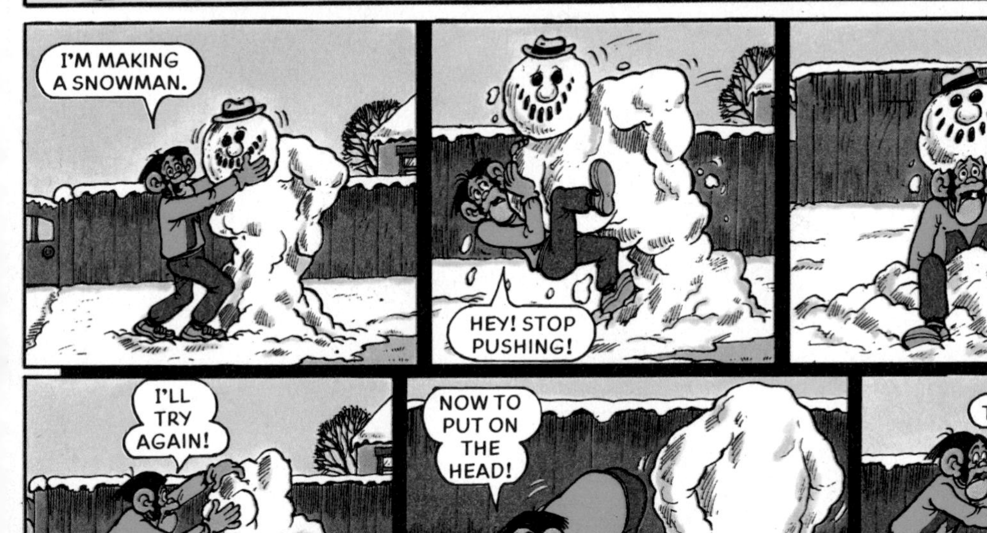

FRED
LET'S SEE IF THERE'S ANYTHING WORTH PINCHING IN TRICKY DICKY'S HOUSE.

THEN—
I KNOW! I'LL PINCH SIDNEY BRAITHWAITE'S SOUP, AN BECOME SOUPER FRED! THEN NO ONE WILL STOP ME! HEH!
SNEAK!

OOGHLE! 'S HORRIBLE!
HA! HA! THAT'S BUBBLE BATH FOR MY MUM! MY SOUP'S AT HOME!

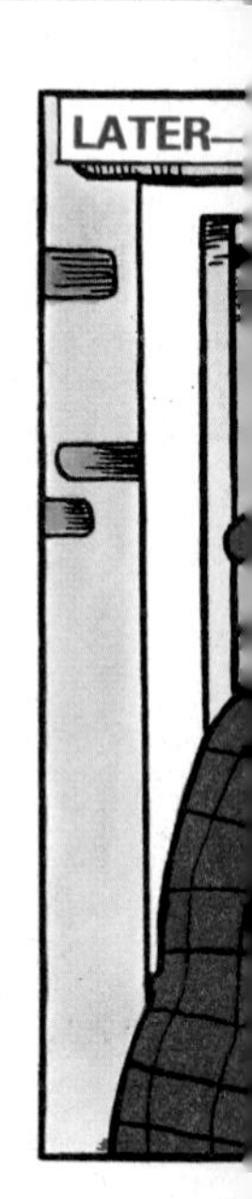
LATER—

GULP! A COPPER! HANG ON—THAT'S AL CHANGE'S HOUSE. I BET IT'S HIM IN DISGUISE!
AL'S HOUSE

AGH!
YOU DON'T FOOL ME! I KNOW YOU'RE WEARING FAKE FLAT FEET!
STOMP!

FLOP

SPLAT!
BOIING!
OGH! I SHOULD'VE
WN! THE PLACE
OOBY-TRAPPED!

D'YOU LIKE MY AUTOMATIC BOOTER-OUTER, FRED? HO! HO! HO!
OUCH!
BOOT!

HEY! I'M IN
JCK! MICKEY'S FORGOTTEN TO LOCK HIS DOOR!
CKEY
HE
NKEY

YOOGH! AN ELEPHANT!
MICKEY THE MONKEY
CRUMP!
THUNDER!

DID YOU SEE AN ELEPHANT COME THIS WAY, FRED? I'M BABY-SITTING FOR THE ZOO.

, FRED! HI, P.C. CAIKE.
HY ARE YOU DANCING IN THE STREET?
GULP! IT WASN'T
AL!

HEH! FRED'S A REAL COMIC!
BAH!

OH, OH! HERE COMES TROUBLE, FINGY— THE BAXTER BULLIES.

WE DON'T THINK MUCH OF YOUR SNOWMAN, TOMMY.
MAYBE WE CAN TURN YOU INTO ONE.
HO! HO! WITH A SNOWBALL OR THREE!

PSST! YOUR FURRY PAL'S NOT HERE, SO WE'VE DECIDED TO GIVE YOU A PROPER PASTING THIS TIME!
I'M READY FOR THEM!

HOO-HOO! AND SO WAS FINGY!
YUK!
YEEPS!

OH, NO! YOU DAFT FING! YOU'VE SWALLOWED ALL MY AMMUNITION.
HA! HA!
HO! HO! HO! TOO BAD, CHUM! TAKE AIM . . . FIRE!

SUDDENLY—
HELP!
OW!
EH?

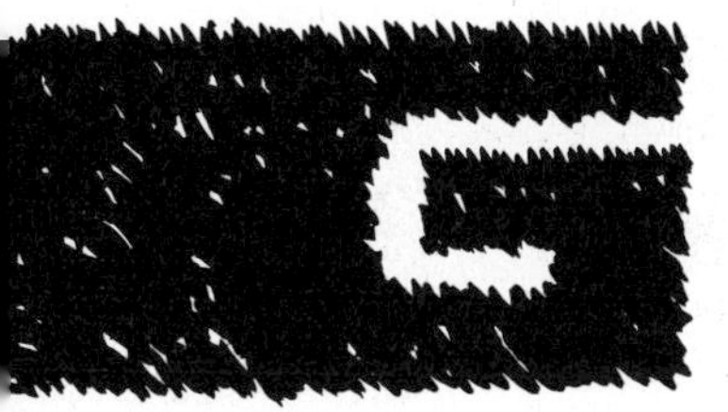

BUT WHEN THE SNOWBALLING STARTS, TOMMY HAS A SECRET WEAPON!
ARGH!
ULK!
WELL DONE, FINGY!
LET'S GO! OOGH!

SOON AFTER, HOWEVER . . .
WE'RE BACK! THAT'S STILL NOT MUCH OF A SNOWMAN!

LISTEN, YOU! LET'S HAVE A PROPER SNOWBALL FIGHT—YOU AND YOUR PAL AGAINST US.
ER—OKAY!

THIS IS GOING TO BE A BIT ONE-SIDED. LOOK AT THEIR HUGE PILES OF SNOWBALLS.

WELL DONE, OLD FING! YOU WERE JUST LIKE A MACHINE-GUN.
PAT! PAT!

YOU ROTTEN FING! WHOSE SIDE ARE YOU ON, ANYWAY?
VERY QUIET SNIGGER!

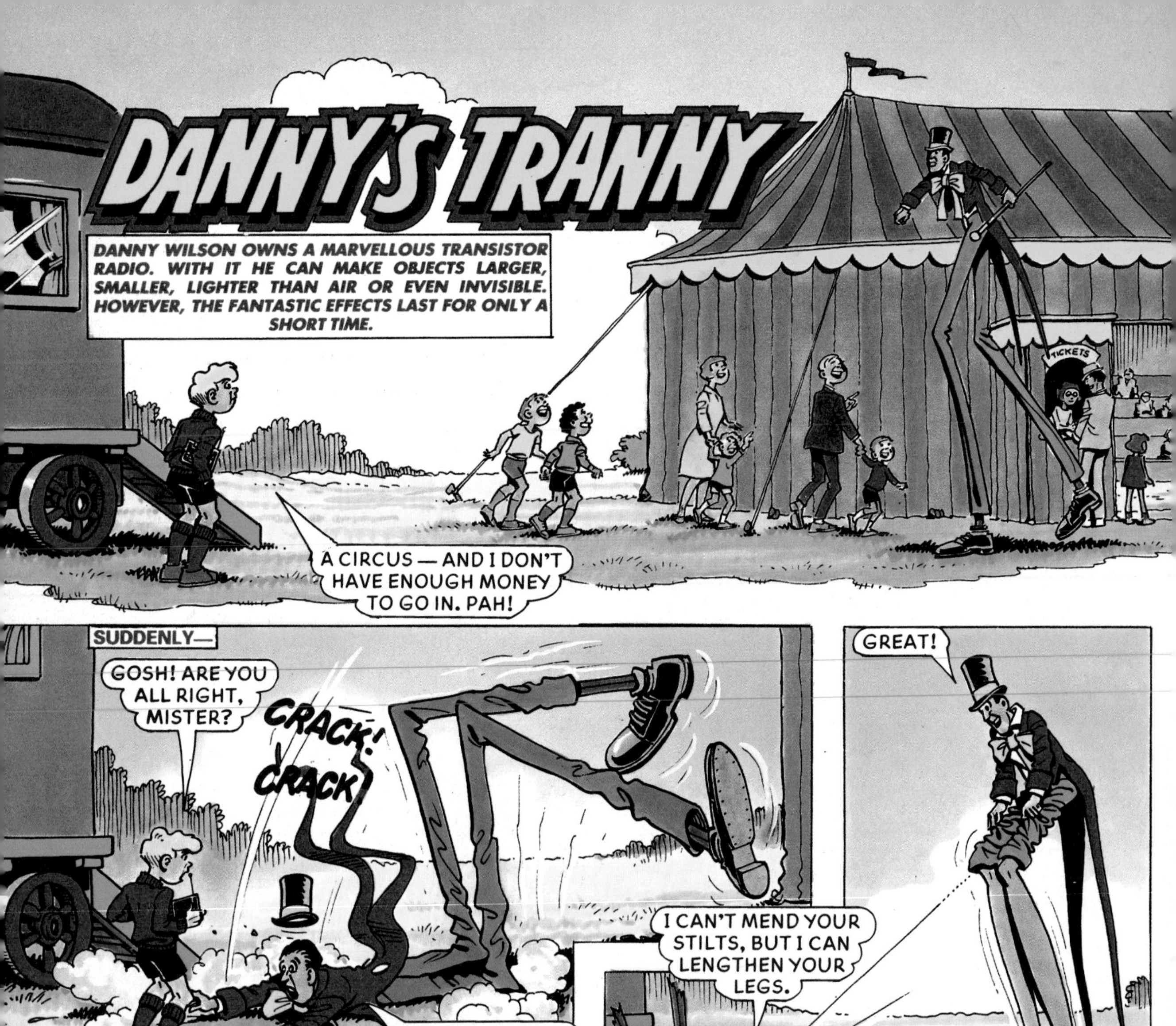
DANNY'S TRANNY
DANNY WILSON OWNS A MARVELLOUS TRANSISTOR RADIO. WITH IT HE CAN MAKE OBJECTS LARGER, SMALLER, LIGHTER THAN AIR OR EVEN INVISIBLE. HOWEVER, THE FANTASTIC EFFECTS LAST FOR ONLY A SHORT TIME.
TICKETS
A CIRCUS — AND I DON'T HAVE ENOUGH MONEY TO GO IN. PAH!
SUDDENLY—
GOSH! ARE YOU ALL RIGHT, MISTER?
CRACK!
CRACK
NO, I'M NOT! MY STILTS HAVE BROKEN. WHAT AM I TO DO?
I CAN'T MEND YOUR STILTS, BUT I CAN LENGTHEN YOUR LEGS.
GROWING RAY
LWS
GREAT!

THANKS, DANNY. NOW I CAN GO AHEAD WITH MY ACT.
HUH! HE MIGHT HAVE OFFERED ME A FREE TICKET.

PRESENTLY, NEARBY—
BOO-HOO! I'M NOT BIG ENOUGH TO SEE THE WILD ANIMALS.
I'LL FIX IT.

VANISHING RAY
VHF
THIS WILL GET RID OF THE CROWD — FAST!

EEK!
THE BARS HAVE GONE!
HO! HO! THE BARS ARE STILL THERE. THEY'RE JUST INVISIBLE.
EEK! IT'LL HAVE US FOR LUNCH!
NOW YOU CAN SEE, EH?
SUPER, DANNY!

THE FLEEING CROWD PANICS ELSIE THE ELEPHANT.
STEADY, ELSIE! STEADY!

OH, NO! SHE'S BOLTING.
EEK!

SO—
SHRINKING RAY
SW
GOTTA DO SOMETHING — FAST!
ICKLE JUMBO!
THE ELEPHANT — IT'S SHRINKING!

SHRUNK JUST IN TIME.
PHEW! YOU'RE A REAL LIFE-SAVER, DANNY.
GAH! GAH!
BOUNCE!

WELL DONE, LAD! YOU DESERVE A FEED AS A REWARD. DOESN'T HE.
BACK TO NORMAL—WELL, NEARLY!
YES — A VERY SPECIAL FEED.

IN YOU GO AND TELL THE RINGMASTER RUFUS AND RUPERT THE CLOWNS SENT YOU IN FOR TEA.
GOSH! RIGHT!

BUT—
HOO-HOO!
I'VE BEEN DIDDLED! IT'S THE CHIMPS' TEA PARTY.
EAT UP, DANNY. HO! HO!

SUDDENLY—
FLOATING RAY
HO! HO! THE TABLES ARE TURNED NOW! I'VE GOT ALL THE GRUB. 'BYEE!
OKAY, OKAY! COME DOWN. IT WAS ONLY A JOKE.

HERE I AM. THE EFFECT'S WORN OFF.

LISTEN, SON — WE COULD DO WITH A FEW NEW TURNS FOR OUR CIRCUS. GOT ANY IDEAS?
HMM . . .? YES, I THINK I CAN HELP YOU.

AND SO—
A FLYING HORSE! GREAT!
THAT'S ONLY THE START. GIVE ME FIVE MINUTES MORE.
FLOATING RAY
MW
AND FIVE MINUTES LATER—
WHAT A SHOW!
FANTASTIC!
FIRE
GREAT WORK, DANNY! THIS IS REALLY PULLING IN THE CROWDS.
COULDN'T HAVE DONE IT WITHOUT MY TRANNY.
RESERVED

AL CHANGE
MASTER OF DISGUISE.
I'M AL. HI!
SO AM I!
I'M SPRY!
AND SO AM I!

HI, MR SPRY! NICE DAY! I'M GONNA HAVE A GO ON THE SWINGS, AN' STUFF.
NOT A BAD IDEA, AL. I THINK I'LL JOIN YOU.

HO! HO! MR SPRY IS REALLY ENJOYING HIMSELF!
YIPPEE!
HOI! WOT'S GOIN' ON 'ERE, THEN?

LESS OF THAT, YOU OLD FOOL! UNDER FOURTEENS ONLY!
AW! WHAT A SHAME! HE WAS ENJOYING HIMSELF.

CHEER UP! I'LL HAVE YOU BACK ON THE CHUTE IN NO TIME.
SIGH!

VERY SOON—
I'VE BROUGHT ALONG MY DISGUISE BAG. I'LL DISGUISE YOU AS A BOY!
COO! WOULD YOU?

HO! HO! HE'LL NEVER GUESS I'M 76 YEARS OLD, WITH THIS DISGUISE!
WHAT?
PLAY AREA

MAVIS! YOU'LL NEVER BELIEVE THIS! ONE OF THOSE BOYS IS AN OLD CHAP IN DISGUISE!
WHAT?
FOOLED HIM!
PLAY AREA

OOH! MY BACK'S SORE, AFTER CARRYING THAT HEAVY DISGUISE BAG.
HUH! SOME DISGUISE! I CAN TELL HE'S AN OLD GEEZER BY THE WAY HE WALKS!

OUT YOU GO, YOU OLD 'UN! YOUR DISGUISE DIDN'T FOOL ME!
OW!

AN' DON'T YOU TRY DISGUISIN' YOURSELF AS ANOTHER BOY! I'LL BE WATCHING!
HMPH!
THERE'S ONE DISGUISE HE WOULDN'T DARE QUESTION, THOUGH.

SO—
AFTERNOON, CHAPPIE! I'M COUNTY SUPERVISOR FOR ALL PLAY AREAS.
GULP! YESSIR!
I'VE COME TO TEST YOUR EQUIPMENT.

AND—
NICE ONE, AL! BUT THE STRAIN OF IT ALL MUST BE TELLING ON YOU — YOU LOOK OLDER THAN ME!
HEH-HEH!

COMPLETELY CUCKOO!

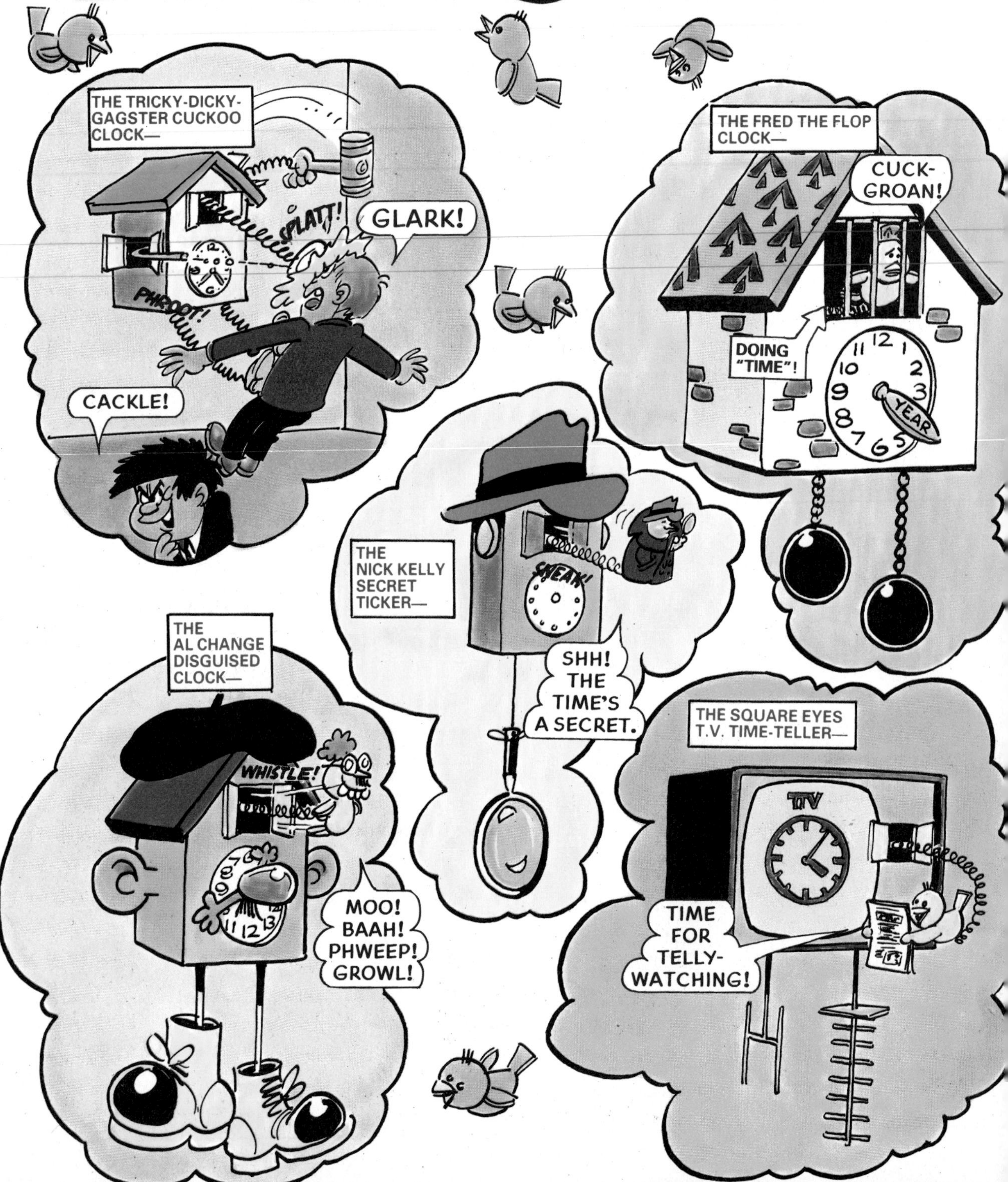

TELLING THE WRONG TIME ISN'T NICE.
CUCK-RASP!
THE JIMMY JINX CLOCK.
THE BERYL THE PERIL PERILOUS TIME-PIECE.
ZIP!
YAAH! BOO TO YOU ALL!
THE HUNGRY HORACE DIET CLOCK—
BYOING!
CLAMP! MISSED AGAIN!
THE SOUPER BOY SOUPER CLOCK—
SOUPER BYOING!
SOUPER SOUP.
I'VE BEEN BUSY WITH MY OWN TRANNY!
DOORS GONE
FLOAT!
THE DANNY'S TRANNIED CLOCK!
FINALLY — THE "TOPPER BOOK" FANS' SPECIAL!
CUCK-COO! HAW! HAW!
TO BE READ ANYTIME!
BOING!
TOPPER

WILLIE WALKER
AND THE WONDERFUL
WHIZZERS from OZZ

In Workchester, England, young Willie Walker was busy playing a game on his computer, when disaster struck!
AW, NO! IT'S GONE ON THE BLINK!
Engrossed, Willie hadn't yet noticed a strange flying craft landing outside his window.

Then—
HI, WILLIE! HAVING TROUBLE WITH YOUR COMPUTER, ARE YOU?
WE'LL HELP!
GOSH! HI, KRIK! HI, KRAK!

Krik and Krak were special chums of Willie's—twins from the land of Whizz, on far-off planet Ozz!
THIS ELECTRONIC WHIZZ-BUG WILL FIX YOUR COMPUTER.

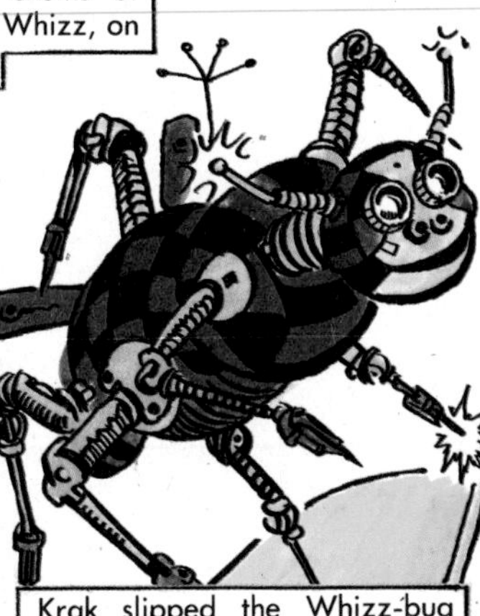
Krak slipped the Whizz-bug into the back of Willie's computer, where, sure enough, it set to work repairing the fault that had developed!

HEY! GREAT! IT'S WORKING AGAIN!
NOW TELL YOUR MUM THAT YOU'RE COMING BACK TO OZZ WITH US FOR A HOLIDAY.

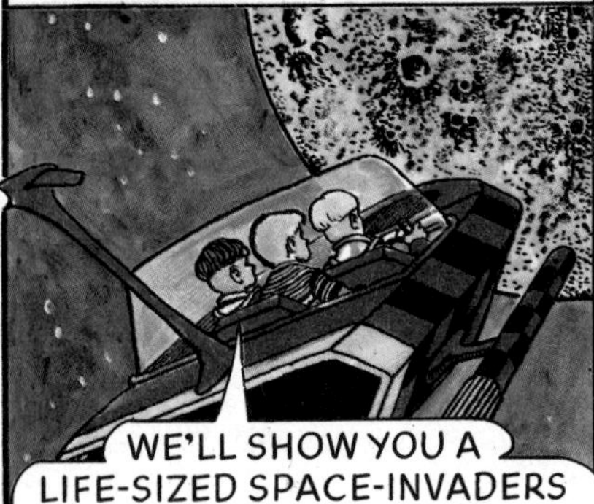
Willie tucked the bug safely into a match box, and very soon the boys were setting off from Earth, to travel millions of miles at faster than the speed of light.
WE'LL SHOW YOU A LIFE-SIZED SPACE-INVADERS GAME ON OZZ! IT'S IN A NEW PLEASURE LAND PARK.

Not long after landing on Ozz, Willie and his chums went along to visit Pleasure Land, which was to be opened by the President that day.
WELCOME PRESIDENT!
PLEASURE LAND
WHAT A PLACE! AND THIS PISTOL YOU HIRED FOR ME — WHAT'S IT FOR?
YOU'LL SOON SEE!

Suddenly, Willie was surrounded by all kinds of weird creatures, seemingly ready to attack him!
IN THIS SECTION, VISITORS FIGHT ELECTRONICALLY-POWERED MONSTERS, MISTER PRESIDENT. WATCH.
G-GULP! WHAT? G-GIANT SPACE INVADERS! GOTTA SHOOT 'EM!
Willie fired rapidly with his gun, but still one of the monsters came on—
SHOOT FASTER, WILLIE!
But Willie missed, and was in for another surprise!
IT . . . IT BURST! BLERSH! WHAT A MESS!
HO! HO! THAT'LL HAPPEN EVERY TIME YOU MISS, WILLIE! THEY'RE NOT REAL, YOU KNOW!
Meanwhile, a sly figure was shining a special ray on some repair-bugs like the one Willie had in his matchbox. Almost instantly the bugs changed colour.
The man was a Kett — a member of a band of super-criminals on Planet Ozz.
THE WHIZZKLEENER WILL TIDY YOU UP, WILLIE.
The Kett tossed the changed bugs into the computer control grille.
And the result was catastrophic—for Willie!
YEOW! IT'S BLOWING INSTEAD OF SUCKING!
The Kett's ray had re-programmed the bugs to RUIN the computer-controlled mechanisms!

In seconds, the whole of Pleasure Land was in a panic, thanks to the work of the Kett's "anti-bugs" in the computer.
GREAT OZZ!
AGH!
BY THE MOONS OF MAZOC!
HELP!
Taking advantage of the confusion, a Kett space-ship swooped down on the President. From it extended a robot arm —
—which whisked the President into the air and up into the space-ship.
HELP!
A KETT-SHIP! IT'S KIDNAPPED THE PRESIDENT!
As the Kett-ship shot off, Willie and the Whizzers scurried to the Whizz-car.
HURRY! LET'S GET AFTER THEM!
Very soon, out in Ozz space—
THEY'RE MAKING FOR THE MAIN FREIGHTER ROUTE!
HOPING TO DODGE OUT OF SIGHT AMONGST THE BIG SHIPS, I RECKON!
Sure enough, the Kett-ship was in the final approach to the main freighter route from Ozz.
HEH! IT WAS ALL SO EASY! WITH YOU AS OUR PRISONER, PRESIDENT, WE CAN FORCE YOUR PEOPLE TO DO ANYTHING WE WISH!
N-NEVER! I WILL DIE FIRST!
YOU JUST MIGHT! CACKLE!

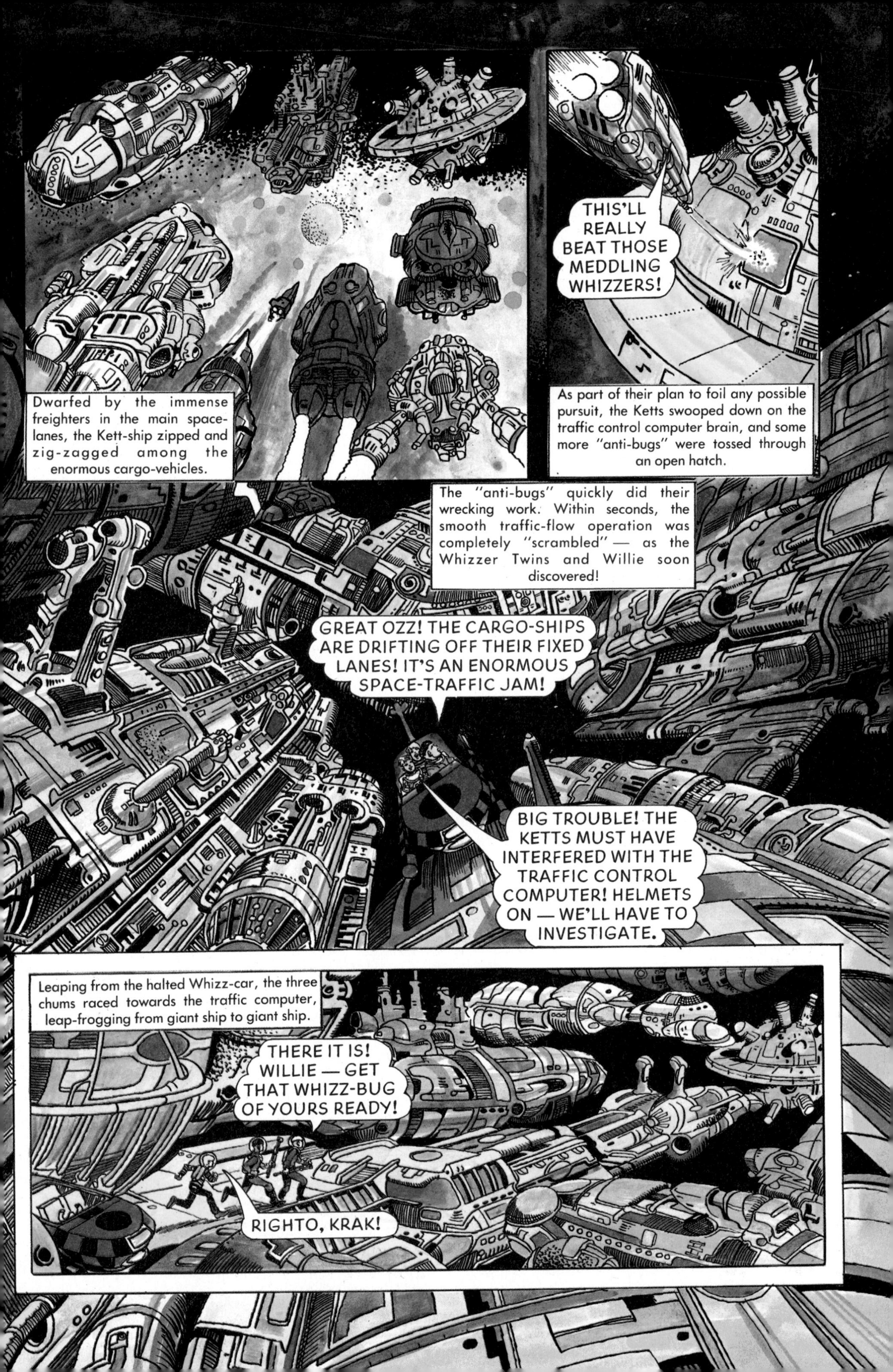
Dwarfed by the immense freighters in the main space-lanes, the Kett-ship zipped and zig-zagged among the enormous cargo-vehicles.
THIS'LL REALLY BEAT THOSE MEDDLING WHIZZERS!
As part of their plan to foil any possible pursuit, the Ketts swooped down on the traffic control computer brain, and some more "anti-bugs" were tossed through an open hatch.
The "anti-bugs" quickly did their wrecking work. Within seconds, the smooth traffic-flow operation was completely "scrambled" — as the Whizzer Twins and Willie soon discovered!
GREAT OZZ! THE CARGO-SHIPS ARE DRIFTING OFF THEIR FIXED LANES! IT'S AN ENORMOUS SPACE-TRAFFIC JAM!
BIG TROUBLE! THE KETTS MUST HAVE INTERFERED WITH THE TRAFFIC CONTROL COMPUTER! HELMETS ON — WE'LL HAVE TO INVESTIGATE.
Leaping from the halted Whizz-car, the three chums raced towards the traffic computer, leap-frogging from giant ship to giant ship.
THERE IT IS! WILLIE — GET THAT WHIZZ-BUG OF YOURS READY!
RIGHTO, KRAK!

Once on the computer's inspection deck, the twins began to set up a strange tripod structure.
PUT THE WHIZZ-BUG INTO THAT HATCH, WILLIE.
IT'LL FIND OUT THE TROUBLE. ONE BUG'S NOT ENOUGH, THOUGH. WE'LL HAVE TO GO IN OURSELVES, TO DO THE REPAIRS.
Setting the co-ordinates for entry to the computer's "brain", Krik then switched on a strange ray, which shrank them to mini-size.
I WONDER WHAT'S GONE WRONG IN THERE?
Inside the circuits of the computer, Krak soon got his answer—
ANTI-BUGS!
The single Whizz-bug would be no match for a whole army of destructive anti-bugs!
DIAL KT-RAY! SHOOT!
The Whizzers' special pistols blasted to bits two of the anti-bugs—
—but another sped past them, and launched itself at Willie.
AGH!
Krak reacted instantly, re-dialling his pistol, firing a great plastic bubble which engulfed Willie!

Under the protective bubble, Willie was safe for the time being. But—
THE ANTI-BUG! IT-IT'S INCREASING PRESSURE! THE BUBBLE'S GOING TO . . .
. . . SHATTER! GOTTA MOVE QUICKLY!
Willie leaped high in the air in a wild bid to escape.
By chance — a very lucky chance — his knee snapped off a small aerial on the anti-bug's back.
Suddenly, the metallic creature twitched—
—and, out of control, cannoned into the others—
—causing them to go berserk, smashing one another to pieces!
The one remaining anti-bug, no longer a threat to the boys, lurched blindly out of the inspection hatch.
OUR WHIZZ-BUG WILL SOON HAVE THE REPAIRS DONE — THEN WE CAN TRACK DOWN THE KETTS, ON-SCREEN.
Outside again—
HMM . . . I'LL KEEP A HOLD OF THIS ANTI-BUG. MAYBE MY WHIZZ-BUG CAN REPAIR IT.

As Willie put the anti-bug in his match-box, the Whizzers brought a scan-screen to life. This quickly showed the Kett ship on a straight course for planet Andraken, in the star-system Strock.
GOSH! HURRY, THEN, TWINS! ACTIVATE THE SPACE-CAR SO WE CAN GET AFTER THEM.
With the computer now repaired, the space-lanes were operating normally.
PHEW! I'M GLAD THERE ARE NO MORE SHIP-JAMS!
At length, the Whizz-car was zooming across the skies of planet Andraken, in search of the Kett-ship. Then . . .
DOWN THERE! LOOK!
COME NO CLOSER, BRATS, OR YOUR PRESIDENT WILL BE ZAPPORATED!
As the Whizz-car landed, out of sight of the Ketts, Willie had an idea.
D'YOU HAVE A SPARE PIECE OF WIRE SOMEWHERE, KRAK?
YES, BUT WHY?
WELL, IF I MAKE A NEW AERIAL FOR THIS ANTI-BUG, WITH THIS WIRE . . .
. . . THEN DROP IT INTO THE KETT SHIP, WE'LL SEE WHAT HAPPENS!
THAT'S US RE-STOCKED WITH FUEL FROM OUR SECRET DUMP. LET'S GO! AND NO TRICKS FROM YOU, PRESIDENT!

HEY, WHIZZERS! ARE YOU LISTENING OUT THERE? IF YOU TRY TO FOLLOW US, THE PRESIDENT WILL BE THROWN OUT OF THE SHIP INTO DEEP SPACE — WITH NO SPACE-SUIT!
Meanwhile, the anti-bug was busy creating havoc in the cosmotronic section of the Kett-ship's power source!
The Kett-craft prepared for take-off. But, as the pilot moved the controls, the ship trembled and shook wildly.
THE SHIP'S BREAKING UP! WH-WHAT'S GONE WRONG?
A-AN ANTI-BUG! HOW DID IT GET IN THERE?
Up above, a Whizz police ship, alerted by Krik and Krak, was gliding in to land.
With their ship wrecked, the Ketts had no choice but to surrender.
POLICE
AN OZZ-MILLION THANKS!
When later, Willie's space holiday came to an end, the President in person saw him off!
Some time later, back in Workchester, England—
THIS IS A GREAT COMPUTER GAME, ALFIE — BUT NOT HALF AS EXCITING AS THE REAL THING!
EH?

HUNGRY HORACE
HEH! LOOKING AT ALL THAT SNOW MAKES ME FEEL HUNGRY. NOBODY ABOUT—IN I GO!
LARDER
SOON—
UMF! I'LL FIX HIM! CACKLE!
LARDER
POUND! POUND!
HORACE! WHAT ARE YOU DOING IN THERE? OPEN UP!
HAR! THAT'S THE DOOR JAMMED.
SPLAT!
BUT—
LIFT!
HEH! IT'S JUST AS WELL I FITTED THIS SPECIAL LIFT-OFF DOOR!
OUTSIDE—
HAR!
DIVERSION
GREAT! IT'S WORKING! HERE COMES THE SNOW-PLOUGH. I'LL JUST LEAVE THE DOOR OPEN AND HEAD FOR THE LARDER.
WHIRR!
RUMBLE!
RUMBLE!
DIVERSION

HOLD IT! I'M ABOUT!
YERK! DAD!
ON REGULAR LARDER PATROL, I AM!
AW!
DRAG!
LARDER
SCUFF!
YIKES!
SCRAM!
WHUMP!
YOWP! HE'S GETTIN' CRAFTIER!
SOON—
CORKS! THE SNOW'S REALLY HEAVY. I HOPE WE'RE NOT SNOWED IN.
I CAN HARDLY SEE WHERE I'M GOING.
SNOWED IN, EH? HMM!
YEEK! HOW?
CRASH!
TUMBLE!
HAR! NOW TO CLOSE THE LARDER DOOR BEFORE THAT AVALANCHE HITS ME.
HORACE! ARE YOU IN THERE? DON'T YOU DARE EAT ANYTHING!
YES, DAD! DON'T HURRY TO DIG ME OUT! HEH! CHOMP!
DIG!
I JUST FOLLOWED THE SIGNS, MISTER. I DON'T KNOW HOW IT 'APPENED.

JOE the JANNY
JOE JONES, SCHOOL JANITOR

PLAYTIME —
OUR SLIDE'S NOT VERY SLIPPY.
I'LL SOON FIX THINGS FOR YOU.

ER, MORNING, SIR.
CATCH!
GASP! THANK YOU, JONES.

WHY ON EARTH HAVE YOU GOT A MOP OUTSIDE?
ER, I THOUGHT IT WAS A BRUSH — NO WONDER IT WASN'T CLEARING THE SNOW!

JONES!
ER, JUST TESTING, SIR. YOU'RE RIGHT — IT IS DANGEROUS!

I'LL JUST PRETEND TO PUT SALT ON THE ICE, KIDS.
WINK!
WHY CAN'T I SEE SALT COMING OUT OF THAT PACKET, JONES? BAH! I'M COMING OUT TO DO THE JOB MYSELF.

THERE! A JOB WELL DONE!
ONLY SNOW, OF COURSE!

PERFECTLY SAFE, NOW — EEP!

HERE 'GO!
MUCH BETTER!
OH-OH! BEWARE OF APPROACHING HEADMASTER!
WHIZZ!
TA, MR JONES.
YAARGH!
SKID!
OH, NO! THE HEAD!
GET RID OF THAT SLIDE AT ONCE! USE LOTS OF SALT.
D'YOU HAVE TO, JANNY?
'FRAID SO!
PITY, THOUGH — IT IS A BRILL SLIDE . . !
WHIZZZZZ!
CHEER UP, KIDS — WE'RE NOT BEATEN YET.
TIP!
THIS'LL FOOL HIM!
SCOOP!
OUT COMES THE HEAD —
GIVE ME THAT PACKET, JONES.
YOU'D BETER PUT ON THESE GLOVES, SIR. SALT CAN BE VERY SORE ON THE HANDS.
I CAN'T UNDERSTAND IT — THAT SLIDE SHOULD BE MELTED BY NOW. OOH! I'M OFF FOR A LIE-DOWN.
BUMP!
GOOD OL' JANNY! HE SAVED OUR SLIDE!
YES. I'M A REAL SLIPPY CUSTOMER!

Another tale for you — where much perilousness is due!

GOOD OLD OIL! SUCCESS!
SHOOT!
FALL!
UGGH!
FLUMP!

SOON —
USING MY CARTIE TO CARRY THE PIANO IS A GREAT IDEA.
STOP CHATTERING AND HELP TO PULL!
PULL!
PULL!
RISE!

ERP! I'M LOSING MY MARBLES.
BERYL!
PICK-UP!

CLUNK!
DON'T LET GO . . . OHH!
PLUMMET!
OOPS!
CRASH!

DAD! STOP PLAYING AROUND. I'LL BE LATE FOR THE CONTEST!
DROP!
AAARGH!
CRUMPF!

ON A BIT MORE —
WE'LL JUST PUSH THE PIANO ON ITS OWN WHEELS.
THERE'S SQUIRTY SUGSY SLOAN.
NYARP!
SHOVE!
RASP!
TRUNDLE.
PPHRRRP TO YOU, BERYL!

HAVE THESE, WEED.
MISSED ME.
GLOIP! BUT NOT ME!
HURL!
SPLAT!

OH, NO! THE PIANO! IT'S NOT MEANT TO BE GOING THAT WAY, DAD.
DON'T WORRY. I'LL STOP IT.

LOOK OUT! ERK! TOO LATE!
WORKMEN
DESPERATE DIVE!
GLEEP!
RUNAWAY PIANO — GLOOP!
BLOOSH!

ONE "QUIET WORD" FROM THE WORKMEN, LATER —
WELL DONE, DAD! YOU GOT IT.
THE WORKMEN WEREN'T TOO PLEASED, THOUGH.
PANT!
GROWLS!

I NEED A REST! PHEW! GASP!
THIS PIANO WOULD MAKE A GREAT CARTIE.
CLAMBER!

WOOPS! IT MOVES FASTER THAN I THOUGHT IT WOULD, THOUGH.
COME BACK!
FAST TRUNDLE!

THIS IS GREAT.
NORRAGAIN!
ZOOM!
GLARF!
JUMP FOR IT!

STOP! PLEASE STOP, PIANO!
LOOK OUT, DAD!
TURN!

TOO LATE!
BLOOFLE!
FLATTEN!!
WHAM!!
ZIP!

EVENTUALLY —
WELL DONE, DAD. WE'VE MADE IT TO THE CONTEST.
TOTALLY SHATTERED!
GLARF! AND NOT A SCRATCH ON THE PIANO. AMAZING!

IN THE HALL —
SMASHING — BEGIN!
PIANO-SMASHING CONTEST
MUSIC TO MY EARS!
PLINKLE!
SMASH!
CROINK!
SHRIEK! SO THIS IS WHAT SHE WANTED THE PIANO FOR!

GURRR! YOU'LL BE A WRECK BY THE TIME I'VE FINISHED WITH YOU!
PIANO-SMASHING CONTEST
HELP! MY DAD'S GONE POTTY! HELLLP!
CHASE!
FLEE!

IN DISGUISE!

SOME EXPERT DISGUISES IN THE DAYS BEFORE AL CHANGE!

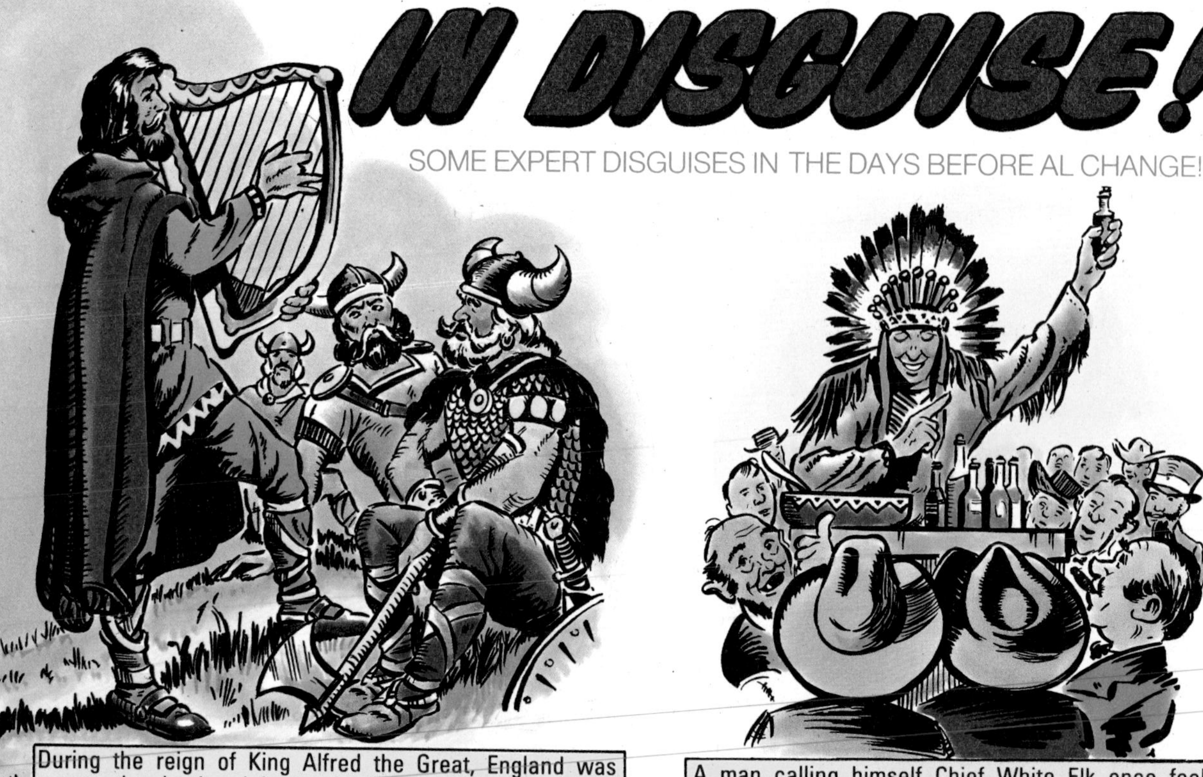

During the reign of King Alfred the Great, England was constantly plundered by raiding Danes. When a Danish army was encamped in the west of England, King Alfred entered their camp disguised as a wandering minstrel and entertained the invaders. But at the same time, he spied out all the secrets of the Danes, and was able later to lead his own army to an easy victory.

A man calling himself Chief White Elk once fooled people all over the United States and Europe by selling bottles he said contained Serpent Oil, a wonderful Red Indian "medicine". He claimed it could cure almost any ailment. He swindled people out of large sums of money before it was discovered that he was just a trickster — a white man, in disguise.

Following the defeat of Charles II by Oliver Cromwell at the Battle of Worcester, in 1651, the King had to escape from the Roundheads. On one occasion he narrowly avoided capture by disguising himself as a stable-lad. After many adventures, he managed to reach France.

King James V of Scotland, who ruled from 1513 to 1542, often went out among his people disguised as a beggar. By speaking to ordinary people who did not suspect that he was their King, he found out all their troubles and did his best to pass laws to put things right! He was a very popular ruler.

After the Battle of Culloden, in 1746, Prince Charles Edward Stuart — "Bonnie Prince Charlie" — was constantly hunted by Redcoats as he tried to escape from Scotland to France. Once, when fleeing from the island of South Uist to Skye, he was forced to travel disguised as a lady's maid. The lady he accompanied was the famous Flora MacDonald.

During World War Two, the Germans were fooled into believing that Field-Marshal Montgomery was in North Africa when he was really in Britain, planning the invasion of Europe. A 'look-alike' disguised as the General took Montgomery's place in North Africa and fooled the German spies.

One of the most amazing jokes in history was played on the Emperor of Germany by a Chinese barber. Germany had demanded that China should send a Royal Prince to apologise for attacks made on Germans in Pekin. The Chinese Royal Family could not face the disgrace of kneeling humbly before a Western ruler. So the barber was sent instead, disguised as a Prince — and he was back in China before the Germans learned that they had been tricked.

Mary Read was a remarkable woman who, disguised as a man, joined the British Army during the reign of Queen Anne. She served first in the infantry, then in the cavalry, fighting in several battles in Europe. At length her secret was discovered and she was discharged from the army. Soon after this she joined a crew of pirates in the West Indies, but was eventually taken prisoner and died in prison in Jamaica.

THE BABE WITH THE INVISIBLE BODYGUARD.

HUP!
NOW BABA GO STRAIGHT OUT FRONT DOOR.
BABA DID IT! NOW BABA GO PLAY IN SANDPIT!
PHEW! NOW I CAN RELAX!
HE'S NICE AN' QUIET . . . EEK! SAND IN MY EYES!
SPLUP!
BABA DIG TO AUSTRALIA.
OUCH! WHO'S GONNA MAKE SURE I DON'T BUMP INTO THINGS?
BUMP!

I'll come with you, Michael!
All you need's a cycle!
PETER PIPER
HIS MAGIC PIPES BRING THINGS TO LIFE!
HIYA, PETER. COMING FOR A RUN?
HOW CAN I, MICHAEL? I HAVEN'T GOT A BIKE.
THIS IS A FUNNY-LOOKIN' BIKE, BUT IT'LL DO. I'LL BRING IT TO LIFE WITH MY MAGIC PIPES . . .
FISH and CHIPPER'S
CIRCUS
IS COMING TO TOWN!
STARRING
CYCLING SID
THE SILLY CLOWN

HERE YOU ARE, PETER. HEE! HEE!
THANKS, SID.

HO! HO! IT'S A BIT TRICKY TO RIDE.
YEEK!
PARP! PARP!

HO! HO! HO! SILLY CLOWN.
CRASH!

I'LL HAVE TO TRY SOMETHING ELSE. HMM . . .
MUSEUM

THE PENNY FARTHING
1863 — 1867
THIS ONE LOOKS GREAT! I'LL BRING IT TO LIFE.

UP YOU GO, YOUNG MAN.
WOW! IT'S HIGH.

ERK! HOW D'YOU CONTROL THIS THING?
WOBBLE!

CRASH!

FOOLISH BOY! GRRR!
WOW! LET'S GO.

A GREAT NEW FILM
THE
TOUR de FRANCE
I'M BOUND TO GET A BIKE OUT OF THIS LOT.
NOW SHOWING AT THE RIO CINEMA

A GREAT NEW FILM THE TOUR de FRANCE
TRING!
ZOOOM!
TRING!
TRING
NOW SHOWING AT THE RIO CINEMA
BONK!
HOI!

HEY! WHY DIDN'T I THINK OF THAT BEFORE?

I'LL BRING THE SHADOW TO LIFE!

HEH! GREAT, EH?
ZOOM!

PRESS!
TRICKY DICKY

HEH! BEWARE OF THE TRICK DOOR, FOLKS.
REAL DOOR

TUM-TI-TUM! WHAT FUN IT IS SELLING JUNK.
AHAR! MY FIRST VICTIM.
GROTTY GOODS CO.

GLERK! WHAT A CHEEKY DOOR!
RASP!
HEE! HEE!
GROTTY GOODS CO.

WHAT'S GOING ON IN THERE?
I WOULDN'T DO THAT, MISTER!

THERE'S A STINK BOMB ON THE OTHER SIDE. TITTER!
YEUCHLE!
GHASTLY PONG!
GROTTY GOODS CO.

BAH! I'LL TRY THIS DOOR ONE MORE TIME.
KNOCK
KNOCK
GROTTY GOODS CO.

HOW DARE YOU BASH ME?
YAROO!
BOOT!
HEE! HEE! 'BYE!

TUM-DA-DOO! TWO PINTS FOR HERE!
CACKLE! HE'S IN FOR A SHOCK.

G-GULP! THE DOOR SEEMS TO BE THIRSTY!
WHIRR!
SLURRP!

OH, GOOD SHOT! TITTER!
GARBLOOSH!
SPLATTER!

WAA! I'M DRENCHED!
STRANGE! IT ISN'T RAINING.
PERFECT! THE POSTIE'S ARRIVED!

AHA! A NEW LETTER-BOX. WE POSTIES NOTICE THAT SORT OF THING.
HE'S ABOUT TO NOTICE SOMETHING ELSE.

COO! WH-WHAT'S THIS?

BLAARFLE!
BASH!
RIP!
IT'S ANOTHER LETTER-BOX. HEE-HEE!

BUT, THEN—
BAH! MUTTER! HEY! THIS ISN'T OUR DOOR! WHASSAT?
CLICK!
SWING!
ULK! D-DAD! TIME TO SCRAM!

HE-HE-HE-HELP!
WHIRR!
WHIRR!
SCOOT!
ERP! WATCH WHERE YOU'RE FLYING TO, DAD!

ONE CRASH LATER—
GROAN! DAD! MOVE OFF!
NOT A HOPE, BOY! I'VE BEEN HEARING ABOUT YOUR TRICKERY.

SO—
EEK! YOU'RE HUGE! PLEASE SAY YOU CAN'T READ!
PANIC.
CALLERS
DON'T RING OR KNOCK UPON THIS DOOR- JUST RAP ON DICKY AND LET HIM ROAR. Signed DAD
PLUMBER
UGH! GRUNT! DIS LOOKS LIKE FUN!

MICKEY THE MONKEY

SEND FOR
Kelly
AND HIS ASSISTANT
CEDRIC
in
THE CASE OF THE PINCHED PARROT
FASTER, CEDRIC! THE MINISTER ASKED TO SEE US URGENTLY.
IT MUST BE AN EMERGENCY. HE WANTS US TO GO STRAIGHT TO HIS HOUSE.

AT THE MINISTER OF SECRET INFORMATION'S HOUSE —
MY PARROT'S BEEN STOLEN.
PARDON? YOUR PARROT?
I THOUGHT THIS WAS URGENT STATE BUSINESS? A LOST PARROT IS HARDLY AN EMERGENCY, MINISTER.

YOU DON'T UNDERSTAND. MY PARROT'S HEARD EVERY SINGLE SECRET I'VE EVER MENTIONED — AND HE REPEATS EVERYTHING HE HEARS!
OH, DEAR!

SO FIND HIM BEFORE HE BLABBERS EVERYTHING!
YES, MINISTER.
WE'LL LOOK FOR CLUES RIGHT AWAY.

LOOK, CEDRIC! FOOTPRINTS — AND ROUND HOLES! THIS SUGGESTS A MAN WITH A WOODEN LEG.

WHERE DO WE START LOOKING FOR A SPY WITH A WOODEN LEG?
THAT STUMPS ME, MR KELLY.

DOWN THE STREET A BIT —
LOOK! SOMEONE WITH A WOODEN LEG HAS STEPPED IN THAT PUDDLE . . .
SOMEONE WITH A STOLEN PARROT, PERHAPS?

THE TRAIL LEADS THROUGH THAT DOOR.
STAGE DOOR

THERE HE IS — BEHIND THAT SCREEN. LET'S GRAB HIM.

YOU'RE UNDER ARREST.
AWRRK!

HOW DARE YOU INTERRUPT MY LONG JOHN SILVER ACT!
WHUMP!
AWRRK!
OOYAH!

A FALSE LEAD, EH?
STAGE DOOR
YEB! AND BY DOSE IS DINGING.

MEANWHILE —
PRETTY POLLY, TELL ME ALL YOUR MASTER'S SECRETS, AND I'LL GIVE YOU A PEANUT.

YOUGH!
WHERE'S MY CAGE? SQUAWK!

AND WHAT OF OUR TWO SLEUTHS? THEY'RE AT A LOSS!
DEPARTMENT STORE
WHAT NOW, CEDRIC?
LET'S GO IN HERE SO I CAN BUY A NEW HAT, MR KELLY. THIS ONE'S RUINED.

AH! A PERFECT FIT!
I WANT A CAGE FOR A PARROT.
WHAT'S THAT?

THAT'S THE MISSING PARROT.
PRETTY POLLY! PRETTY POLLY.
OH, NO! IT'S THAT PEST, KELLY!

I'VE GOTTA GET AWAY FAST. THIS'LL DO.
HE HAS A WOODEN LEG, MISTER KELLY.
SEEFORE ELECTRIC TRIKE G.T.
AC/DC

GRAB THE OTHER CAR, CEDRIC. WE'LL GIVE CHASE IN THAT.

STOP, THIEVES!
DRAT! THEY'RE STILL AFTER ME.

I'LL DODGE IN HERE— UNDER THE BARRIER.

SUPER STOCK CAR RACING
YEEARGH! IT'S A RACE-TRACK!

CRASH!

GREAT! WE'VE GOT HIM NOW, MR KELLY.
AWRK!
BUT THE BIRD'S FLOWN!

LOCK HIM UP, OFFICER! HE'S A NASTY SPY.
ZOOLOGIC GARDE
LOOK, MR KELLY — THE PARROT'S FLYING INTO THE ZOO.
IN WE GO, THEN, AND START LOOKING!
POLLY! PRETTY POLLY!
TICKETS
WHERE CAN HE BE?
IN THE BIRD HOUSE, MAYBE?
SUDDENLY —
— AND HERE'S ANOTHER TOP SECRET. THE PRIME MINISTER SAID . . . AWRRK!
!
. . . AWRRK! THERE ARE WEAPONS IN THE CELLAR AT THE UNBAWANGA EMBASSY . . . THAT'S A SECRET!
PARROT HOUSE
HE'S IN THE PARROT-HOUSE —
— BLABBING!
AND HERE'S ANOTHER TOP SECRET THAT THE MINISTER MENTIONED IN HIS SLEEP . . .
LATER —
SORRY, MINISTER, BUT I HAD TO BRING THEM ALL. YOUR PARROT BLABBED, AND NOW THE LOT OF THEM KNOW YOUR SECRETS.
AWRRK!
OH, NO!
AWRK!
EEEEH!
PIECES OF EIGHT! PIECES OF TEN!
MEOW!
RIP!

JIMMY JINX
GOODIE
BADDIE
AND WHAT HE THINKS

YIPPEE! HERE GOES FOR ANOTHER DAY OF SLIDING AN' SKATING AN' SLEDGING!

AW!
SORRY, JAMES! IT'S MELTED!
NEVER MIND! I KNOW WHERE YOU CAN SLIDE!

SHOES OFF, JIM—THE HALL FLOOR'S NICE AN' SLIPPY!
I DON'T THINK THAT'S A GOOD IDEA!

WHEEEE!
S-SKID!

HAR! GREAT! I LIKE A BIT OF A MESS!
TIP!
YEEK!
CATCH!
I DON'T!

THAT WAS YOUR FAULT, BADDIE!
HAH! JIM WAS ONLY HAVIN' A BIT OF FUN!

YOU NEED MORE PRACTICE, JIM. GET YOUR MARBLES OUT, AN' SHOES BACK ON.

HEH! NOT BAD, EH?
THIS IS EXTREMELY DANGEROUS!
ROLL!

THAT WAS YOUR FAULT AGAIN, BADDIE!
RUBBISH!
CRASH!
SLIP!

ROLLER-SKATES ARE BEST, EH, JIM? DO A BACKWARD TRUNDLE.
TRUNDLE!
LOOK OUT!

DON'T SAY IT! WHY DON'T YOU THINK OF SOMETHING FOR JIM TO TRY?
THUD!
BUMP!
WHOOSH!
OKAY! I KNOW SOMETHING VERY SAFE! LET'S GO!
EH? WHERE?

DRY SKI SLOPE
JAMES CAN'T COME TO HARM HERE!
OH, NO!
LET'S GET THIS LOT SHIFTED.
WHIZZ!

WON'T COME TO ANY HARM, EH? PHOOEY! YOUR SCHEMES ARE JUST AS BAD AS MINE!
ZIP!
HEY! I WAS JUST GONNA MOVE THAT!

DESERT ISLAND DICK

THOSE WERE THE DAYS!
SOME SCENES FROM HISTORY.
THE WARS OF THE ROSES.
UGH!
OOF!
THE COLOSSEUM, ROME.
THIS IS A GREAT CIRCUS!
THE MANAGER WASN'T JOKING WHEN HE SAID HE'D LEND ME A HAND TO KEEP OFF THE LION!
THE BLACK PRINCE —
SPLOSH!
— AND HOW HE GOT HIS NAME!
AARGH — GLUB!
I HATE MUDDY BATTLEFIELDS!
THE GREAT WALL OF CHINA.
BEST CHINA VERY FRAGILE
TUT! TUT! ANOTHER CLACK!
A RARE PORTRAIT OF ETHELRED THE UNREADY.
STOP PAINTING! I'M NOT READY YET!
ETHELRED THE UNREADY
THE HUNDRED YEARS WAR.
THIS WAR ISN'T HALF DRAGGING ON. I TOLD MY WIFE I'D BE HOME FOR TEA!

ONE QUIET DAY IN WIGGLEY WOOD —
HEEL, TIDDLES.
TIDDLES.
NORMAN NIRGLE, A QUIET CHAP.
I'LL PULL THIS BRANCH OFF AND THROW IT FOR YOU, TIDDLES — EEK!
HANDS OFF, CHUM!
"FEARFUL FUN-TALK
REE" CHEERS
GLEEGLE!
NO, I'LL PUT YOU UP!
TOSS!
BOOM!
WOTSAT? YELP! LIGHTNING!
KABOOM!
I P-PROMISE NOT TO UPSET YOU ANY MORE, IF YOU JUST HELP ME!
HMM! RIGHTO!
BACK AT NORMAN'S —
WELL, I KNOW IT LOOKS RIDICULOUS . . .